LONG LIVE BART'S

1st published in 2013 by Obelisk Books,

Tarvers Orchard, Sutton-under-Brailes, Banbury, OX15 5BH.

Tel. 01608 685 778

greta.barnes@zen.co.uk

Printed by Berforts Information Press Oxford

ISBN: 978-0-9557206-3-5

978-0-9557206-4-2 (hardback edition)

ACKNOWLEDGEMENTS

First and foremost I would like to thank Ruth Midgley for her advice and encouragement and for her invaluable editorial input into *Long Live Bart's*. Many thanks also go to Lynne Brown for her splendid design work. Working with these two has been a pleasure.

William Shand deserves my appreciation and thanks for his careful reading of and comments on the book, as do Christopher Gummer, Sybil Allen and Mary Walker.

Katie Ormerod, the archivist at Bart's, has fielded my queries with great patience. I am most grateful to her and to St Bartholomew's Hospital Archive Department for permission to use their images.

It would not have been possible to undertake the time-consuming tasks of researching and writing *Long Live Bart's* without the support of my husband David.

Central cover illustration: The Fountain at Bart's, detail from a watercolour by Rose Barton, 1892

Samuel Gee

Robert Morrison

Thomas Young

E. Bedford Fenwick

Luther Holden

John Lyle

Elizabeth Blackwell

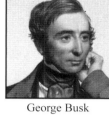
William Harvey

James Hinton

William Pitcairn

Erasmus Wilson

LONG LIVE BART'S

THE EARLY YEARS

Stories of St Bartholomew's Hospital in the City of London 1123–1900

Greta Barnes

George Busk

Richard Owen

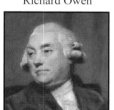
Percivall Pott

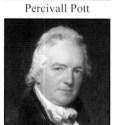
John Abernethy

Isla Stewart

John Leech

Maria Machin

William Hogarth

Thomas Smith

William Lawrence

Frederic Skey

INTRODUCTION

St Bartholomew's Hospital, founded in 1123, is the oldest hospital in Britain which still occupies its original site and which has never closed its doors. Over its nearly 900 years of existence Bart's has twice faced the real possibility of closure: once during the Reformation in the 16th century, when it was the only general hospital in England to survive, having been saved at the behest of King Henry VIII; and again in the 1990s as part of the National Health Service Hospital Reforms, when, after a long running battle, it was rescued chiefly due to the Save Bart's Campaign.

Several erudite and lengthy books about Bart's have been written previously, and all give excellent in-depth information about the hospital and its history. These tomes provided me with valuable background information for my earlier books, *Scissors, Nurse, Scissors* and *The Heart of Bart's*. However, I found myself wanting to know more about the men and women who had, in one way or another, been associated with the hospital since its foundation.

These days it is popular to refer to personal 'journeys'. *Long Live Bart's: The Early Years* is the first part of my journey through the centuries to find out about some of the colourful Bart's characters. Many were responsible for the 'ups', and for making the hospital a national treasure, and others for the 'downs', including several who brought the hospital into disrepute. There are many other individuals whom I would

Volumes containing minutes and orders from meetings of the Hospital governors

have liked to have included, but sadly space was limited and difficult decisions had to be made.

Long Live Bart's has been written chiefly to entertain and to enlighten readers about Bart's through its people. Whilst I have tried to be as accurate as possible, some of the tales are clearly apocryphal. Not surprisingly there is less information available about people during the very early years, but one of the purposes of the book has been to try and provide a flavour of the changes and background to medical and nursing 'society' in London over the years. It is noticeable that women do not get much of a look in until the late Victorian era when feminism begins to make its mark.

My time as a student nurse at Bart's was fleeting and many years ago, but I will never forget the sense of history I experienced the first time I walked into the famous Gibbs square and entered the hospital with its kindly, healing walls. Long Live Bart's!

CONTENTS

GRANT MADE BY RAHERE TO HAGNO THE CLERK

The greatest treasure of St Bartholomew's Hospital, and the earliest document in the Hospital Archives, is the Deed of Rahere, from 1137. By this deed, Rahere, founder of the Hospital, granted the Church of St Sepulchre to Hagno the Clerk, his successor as Master of the Hospital. The seals affixed to the deed in the presence of Rahere are still attached.

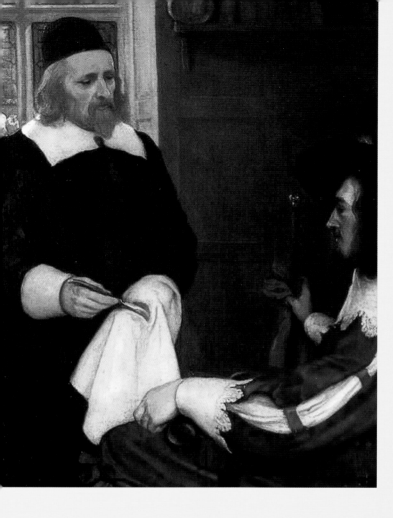

1

THE MIDDLE AGES, TUDORS AND STUARTS

Smithfield was a dark and marshy place in the 12th century, with a murky past, but it was here that Rahere the monk was directed by a vision of St Bartholomew to found a hospital and a priory to care for the sick, the poor and the wandering homeless.

During the first three centuries of its existence there is only sparse information about the hospital and the people connected with it. But we do know of some individuals who became famous or infamous in those medieval times. There are gruesome tales of murder and conspiracy, including the hanging, drawing and quartering of William Wallace outside the hospital gates, and the macabre murder of Wat Tyler in a chamber inside Bart's.

More is known about the hospital under the Tudors and the Stuarts. These centuries too were not without drama: the Bart's physician Dr Roderigo Lopez was executed for plotting to poison Queen Elizabeth I. Others became famous for more respectable reasons. Two medical men of great note were the surgeon Thomas Vicary, who was vital to the survival and successful re-founding of the hospital, and William Harvey, perhaps the most famous of all, who was the first person to describe the circulation of the blood. The heroine of the Great Plague, Matron Margaret Blague, is also remembered.

RAHERE c.1090–1144

Court jester, Augustinian canon and founder of Bart's Hospital

The founding of St Bartholomew's Hospital, in 1123, during the reign of William the Conqueror's youngest son, Henry I, was an act of thanks to God from a reprobate cleric made good. According to legend, Rahere's selfless action followed a near-fatal illness and a vision in which St Bartholomew directed him to build a church and a hospital in Smithfield. Nearly 900 years later, Rahere's hospital has never closed its doors, making it the oldest hospital in Britain still occupying its original site.

It is probable that Rahere came from a poor family, which was not a good start in life particularly in medieval times. However, in spite of this he grew up being noticeably ambitious and charming as well as fun loving and intelligent. As a young man he was able to make many rich and powerful friends and it was through these friends that he joined the court of King Henry I.

A description of Rahere's life at court is to be found in *The Book of Foundation*, which was written fairly shortly after his death and was based on the recollections of people who actually knew him:

'... he approached the king's palace with some frequency and resorted to the tumults of that tumultuous court, and with jocular flattery desired to attract to himself with ease the hearts of many. There he made it his business all day long to attend spectacles, banquets, jests and the rest of the trifles of the court ... he was well known to, intimate with, and a comrade of the king and of the great men of the court.'

It seems likely from this description that Rahere was, as legend suggests, the King's jester and/or musician. However, the name Rahere also appears in a list of canons at St Paul's Cathedral in 1115.

Rahere's resolve

Rahere's fun-loving life ended in 1118 with the death of Queen Matilda, of whom Rahere was very

Rahere kneels before St Bartholomew, patron saint of the hospital

fond. This had a profound effect on him – as did the sinking of the White Ship in the English Channel two years later, which took the life of King Henry's son and heir as well as several other members of the Royal Family. Rahere realised that there was more to life than merrymaking and resolved to live a more worthy life.

Pilgrimage to Rome

The reformed Rahere set out on a long and arduous journey to Rome. Once there, in order to renounce his sins and to pray for remission of them, he visited the places associated with the martyrdoms of St Peter and St Paul. While in Rome, he contracted 'Roman Fever' (thought to be malaria). Rahere was critically ill and was sure he was going to die but felt that he had not yet given sufficient satisfaction to God to atone for his past sins. He vowed that if he recovered and was able to return to England he would found a hospital for the poor in London. His prayer was answered and once he was fit enough he started on his long journey home.

Rahere's vision

While on his way back, Rahere had a very frightening vision in which he saw a beast with four feet and two large wings. The beast lifted him up and put him on a ledge overhanging a deep abyss

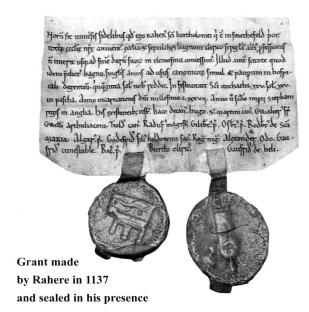

Grant made by Rahere in 1137 and sealed in his presence

containing a bottomless pit. Rahere was absolutely petrified, believing he was going to plunge headlong into the unfathomable pit. All too aware of his past sins and of what would happen if he fell into the pit, Rahere screamed in terror.

Suddenly a figure appeared before him, saying that he was St Bartholomew, an apostle of Jesus Christ, and that he had come not only to save Rahere but also to tell him that he had chosen a spot for Rahere to site his hospital and that he should also build a church. Both institutions were to be erected at a place called Smedfield (Smithfield) in London and both were to bear the name of Saint Bartholomew as their patron saint. St Bartholomew continued by telling Rahere that he would take care of all things financial and that as long as Rahere worked hard he was not to worry about the expense of the project and that nothing would stand in his way. At this the vision disappeared and Rahere decided it had indeed been a heavenly command from St Bartholomew.

The founding of Bart's

Rahere made his way back to London knowing he now had to found both a hospital and a church, which was a huge undertaking. On his return he discovered that Smedfield was part of the King's Market and that he required permission from King Henry to build on the land. Fortunately, Rahere had great support from Richard, the Bishop of London, and together they went to see the King. Permission was granted with ease (the apostle was true to his word) and Rahere was authorised to go ahead. There was no problem concerning the cost of the construction of the hospital and church. This was due in the main to the patronage of the King and the Bishop but also because Rahere managed to obtain a charter to hold an annual fair to boost funds. The fair was to be held each year on St Bartholomew's Feast Day, 24 August, and became known as the Cloth Fayre. St Bartholomew was true to his word and it would seem that nothing stood in Rahere's way, for the building of both St Bartholomew's Hospital and the Priory Church of St Bartholomew the Great started at the same time in 1123.

Rahere was both Prior of the Priory and Master of the Hospital, although it is probable that from about 1137 the administration of the hospital was carried out under his direction by Hagno the Clerk. The earliest document possessed by the hospital is a document by which Rahere granted Hagno the Church of St Sepulchre in return for an annual payment of 50 shillings for the use of the canons and the poor in St Bartholomew's Hospital. Rahere died on 20 September 1144 and is buried by the altar in the church of St Bartholomew the Great.

Rahere's tomb in the church of St Bartholomew the Great

WILLIAM WALLACE c. 1270–1305

Scottish hero hanged, drawn and quartered at Smithfield

One of Scotland's greatest heroes, William Wallace was a daring leader in the bitter struggle to win back Scottish independence from King Edward I of England. Despite initial successes, the Scottish opponents of English domination were ultimately crushed while Wallace himself was captured, tried for treason and then subjected to a barbaric death in front of St Bartholomew's Hospital.

William Wallace window, chapel to St Margaret, Edinburgh Castle

Before turning to Scotland, King Edward I had already succeeded in bringing Wales under English rule. Encouraged by this, he took advantage of a succession crisis in Scotland in 1296 to impose himself as ruler north of the border. This led to great unrest among the Scots and William Wallace became one of the main leaders during the Wars of Scottish Independence.

Wallace enjoyed a major victory over the English at the Battle of Stirling Bridge in 1297. This was followed by other military successes and Wallace was rewarded by being appointed 'Guardian of the Kingdom' and receiving a Scottish knighthood.

However, Wallace's fortunes changed in 1298 when he was defeated by the English near Falkirk. He escaped from the battle but his military reputation was badly damaged. Later that year he resigned as 'Guardian' to be succeeded by Robert the Bruce. It is thought that Wallace then went abroad for a time, probably to France.

Capture, trial and execution

On his return to Scotland in 1303 Wallace discovered that a bounty had been offered by King Edward to anyone who killed or captured him. Although he successfully avoided capture for a time and took part in a couple of skirmishes in 1304, he was seized by a Scottish knight loyal to Edward and handed over to the English near Glasgow in 1305.

Wallace was taken to London where he was tried in Westminster Hall for treason and for atrocities against English civilians in war. Found guilty, he was taken to the Tower of London, where he was stripped naked and chained prostrate to a hurdle before being be pulled by two horses through the city to Smithfield while being mocked and stoned by the public.

It was here, by St Bartholomew's Hospital, that William Wallace met his end. According to the custom for dealing with traitors, he was hanged but released while still alive and then emasculated, disembowelled, beheaded and quartered. His limbs were displayed in Newcastle, Berwick, Stirling and Perth and his head placed on London Bridge.

Memorial plaque to Scotland's hero, outside St Bartholomew's Hospital

WAT TYLER 1341–1381

Peasant leader wounded at Smithfield and murdered at St Bartholomew's Hospital

Wat Tyler was the leader of the English Peasants' Revolt of 1381 – a rebellion against the introduction of a poll tax. He died as the result of an unprovoked attack by the Lord Mayor of London.

After marching to London with his fellow rebels, Tyler met the young King Richard II on 14 June 1381 and the King agreed to the peasants' demands. However, on hearing that the rebels had murdered the Archbishop of Canterbury, Richard changed his mind. The next day, while meeting the King at Smithfield, Tyler was badly wounded by the Lord Mayor, Sir William Walworth, and one of the King's men.

According to tradition, Tyler did not die at once but was taken to St Bartholomew's Hospital and put in the Master's chamber. There, on Walworth's orders, a wound in Tyler's neck was extended – and caused his death. Tyler's body was then taken back to Smithfield, where his head was cut off in front of his followers and displayed on a pole to the King.

Death of Tyler, from the 14th-century Froissart's Chronicles

RICHARD WHITTINGTON 1354–1423

Lord Mayor of London and a benefactor of Bart's

Sir Richard Whittington was a wealthy merchant and Lord Mayor of London. He was the inspiration for the pantomime character Dick Whittington.

Richard Whittington, a younger son of wealthy parents, left Gloucestershire to make his fortune in the City of London. There he became a successful trader of valuable fabrics, and also a money lender, with kings Richard II, Henry IV and Henry V as customers.

Having joined the City Council in 1384, Whittington was made Alderman and then Sheriff in 1393. When the incumbent Lord Mayor died in June 1397, Richard II appointed Whittington to replace him. The people of London confirmed the King's choice, electing Whittington Lord Mayor on four occasions. In 1416 he became an MP. Whittington was seen to be a man who

Richard Whittington commemorated in a statue at London's Royal Exchange

combined enterprise with benevolence and he financed many public works, including new drainage and sanitation.

On his death, in 1423, he left a great deal of money to charity, and the charitable trust he created nearly 600 years ago is still helping people today.

His executors paid for the construction of a south gate to St Bartholomew's Hospital, on which the Whittington arms were placed, and also a stone column adjoining the chapel. As well as being a memorial to Whittington, these works also covered arrears owed by Whittington to the hospital for the rent of his mansion in Le Ryole, a nearby street.

THOMAS VICARY c.1490–1562

Master of the Company of Barbers and Surgeons and Serjeant-Surgeon to King Henry VIII

Thomas Vicary, a barber-surgeon, played a prominent role in uniting the separate guilds of barbers and surgeons into a single livery company. He was also a major figure in the re-founding and running of St Bartholomew's Hospital after King Henry VIII's break with Rome.

Thomas Vicary was born in the county of Kent, where he became a surgeon. After apparently gaining his expertise solely by experience, he rose from obscurity when King Henry VIII complained of sore legs during a visit to Maidstone. Vicary was called in as the local surgeon and managed to effect a cure, which impressed Henry so much that he shortly afterwards invited him to become Serjeant-Surgeon to the Royal Household. Vicary took up the position in 1535 or 1536 – for which he was paid £20 a year (fairly regularly) – and in this capacity was able to advance the reputation of surgeons in England. He was clearly good at this job, as,

Detail from Hans Holbein's 'Henry VIII and the Barber-Surgeons', with Vicary receiving the Act of Parliament

despite all the political upheavals, he was kept on as royal surgeon by Edward VI, Queen Mary I and Queen Elizabeth I.

Master of the Barbers and Surgeons

The importance of Thomas Vicary in bringing to fruition Henry VIII's amalgamation of the Barbers and Surgeons into a single Company in 1540 was enormous. A famous painting by Hans Holbein shows him receiving from Henry VIII the Act of Parliament by which the Company of Barbers and Surgeons was created. He would go on to be Master of the new Company four times.

Vicary introduced the first formal teaching of anatomy at the Barbers and Surgeons' Company and obtained the annual right to the bodies of four executed criminals to dissect for learning purposes. A book entitled *The Anatomie of Mans Body* was published under Vicary's name but was based on an earlier anonymous work. It was the first textbook of anatomy published in English and was a useful dissecting guide for those who were not proficient in Latin. Barber-surgeons and their apprentices were not university graduates and the book in their own language proved a great success.

The re-founding of the hospital

When Henry VIII was refused a divorce from his first wife by the Pope, he responded by taking over the church in England and destroying the monasteries. The Priory of St Bartholomew's closed in 1539 and the monastic organisation ended. The hospital was allowed to continue but it could barely function. This led citizens of London, spearheaded by the Lord Mayor, to petition the King as they were extremely concerned about the provision for the sick poor and the risk of plague.

It is not known why Henry suddenly decided to preserve Bart's but it is likely that Vicary, the King's distinguished surgeon, played a major role. In 1546–47 the King signed a charter granting the Royal Hospital of St Bartholomew to the City of London and endowing it with properties and income. Under the terms of the charter there was to be 'one Matron [paid £3.34 per year] and twelve women [paid £2 each a year] under her, to make the beds and wash and attend upon' the patients. The charter remained in force until the creation of the NHS in 1948.

Vicary's name appears for the first time in connection with Bart's in 1548. The City records for that year show that he was appointed to be a governor of the newly established 'Hospital of the Poor' formerly known as St Bartholomew's Hospital. In 1554 he was appointed the first Superintendent, a post which he held until he died. Vicary lived in a house within the hospital's walls and took a very active part in its administration. He supervised all the paid officials and in 1558 put before the Board 'certen articles for the good order of the poore'. By 1552 a book called *The Order of the Hospital of St Bartholomew* claimed that Bart's had 'healed the pox, fistulas, filthy blains and sores', had 800 patients and cared for 172 people who died in hospital and otherwise 'might have died and stunk in the eyes and noses of the City'.

In 1561, at the age of 71, Vicary and his wife Alice took a joint lease of a house belonging to the hospital in Long Lane. It was there, near his beloved hospital, that Vicary died a year later. To this day, the Royal College of Surgeons maintains an annual lecture in his honour.

HISTORY OF THE COMPANY OF BARBERS AND SURGEONS

Barber-surgeons were medical practitioners working in Europe from medieval times. They usually learnt their trade as an apprentice or from a more experienced colleague. Many were illiterate and had received no formal learning. Their main tasks were letting blood, extracting teeth, performing enemas and surgery, selling medicines and cutting hair.

In England, barbers and surgeons originally had their own separate guilds but in 1540 these were merged by Henry VIII to form the Company of Barbers and Surgeons. Under the terms of the merger, English barbers and surgeons were not permitted to undertake each other's work. To distinguish between the two, the barber's pole was red, white and blue while the surgeon's was red and white to reflect the blood and napkins used to clean up during blood letting.

Over time, the two professions grew farther apart as the status of the surgeons grew and barbers stopped carrying out any surgery. By 1745 all surgeons were university educated and the two groups were finally separated when George II established the London Company of Surgeons, which later became the Royal College of Surgeons of England. The Company of Barbers was allowed to keep the livery hall in the City of London, as well as the Company's treasures, but their involvement in the barbering trade decreased over the years.

Today, the Worshipful Company of Barbers maintains its connection with medicine, especially surgery, and between one third and one half of the livery are members of the medical profession.

ROBERT BALTHROPE 1522–1591

Sartorially elegant Serjeant-Surgeon to Queen Elizabeth I

Robert Balthrope served Queen Elizabeth I as a Serjeant-Surgeon for 30 years. His splendid memorial is in the church of St Bartholomew the Less.

Balthrope was destined to do well in life having served his apprenticeship under Nicholas Alcocke (a prominent member of the Company of Barbers and Surgeons when it was established in 1540).

As a surgeon at Bart's, Balthrope lived in the hospital and could often be seen walking majestically across its court dressed in black satin and a cloth cloak laid with lace and faced with velvet. In 1562 he was appointed one of the Queen's Serjeant-Surgeons, a post he held until his death.

Balthrope was well educated and translated the surgery books of Tagaultius and Ambroise Paré into English. He was Master of the Company of Barber Surgeons in 1565 and 1573.

He was generous with his weath and gave a considerable sum to the poor of the parish of Bart's the Less. When he died he left medicines, books, instruments, bottles, boxes and pots for the use of 'the sicke and sore people' in Bart's and St Thomas's hospitals.

WILLIAM CLOWES 1544–1604

Surgeon to the Fleet fighting the Spanish Armada

The surgeon William Clowes of St Bartholomew's Hospital was a patriotic, devoted servant of Queen Elizabeth I who served his country well.

William Clowes was from a Warwickshire family of sufficient importance to have its own coat of arms and crest. Aged 12 he was sent to London and was admitted by the Company of Barbers and Surgeons to be an apprentice to the surgeon George Keble. After his apprenticeship he served with both the army and the navy, where he became a specialist in syphilis.

In 1576 he was elected surgeon assistant at Bart's and in 1577 was mainly responsible for a new edition of Vicary's book on anatomy. Clowes was promoted to full surgeon in 1581 but resigned three years later when recalled to Her Majesty's forces. In 1588 he was made Surgeon to

England's *Ark Royal* engaged in battle with Spain's *Medina Sidonia*

the Fleet and was 'on duty' on the flagship *Ark Royal* during the great victorious battle against the Spanish Armada. On release from naval duty he was appointed a Serjeant-Surgeon to the Queen and was also on the Court of the Company of Barbers and Surgeons, where he gave lectures to junior colleagues.

William Clowes was not an academic but his six books show he made accurate observations and could support them with reasoned arguments. He was well aware of 'false' surgeons who caused the unnecessary deaths of their patients and was one of the first to show that surgery was changing from a trade to a profession.

RODERIGO LOPEZ 1525–1594

Court physician executed for allegedly trying to poison Queen Elizabeth I

Roderigo Lopez was the first house physician to be appointed at St Bartholomew's Hospital. He became physician to Queen Elizabeth I and was convicted of high treason.

A 1627 book illustration suggests there was no doubt that the executed Lopez had plotted to poison his Queen

Roderigo Lopez was born in Portugal and raised as a New Christian (Jewish and Muslim converts). Making no secret of his Jewish roots, Lopez moved to London in 1559 to escape the Portuguese Inquisition. He was appointed as house physician at Bart's, where William Clowes, then a well-known Bart's surgeon, was impressed with his ability. Lopez's duties included attending the poor of the hospital twice a week. Lopez and his wife Sara had five children, all baptised in the hospital church.

Queen's physician

Although Lopez became a member of the College of Physicians, he was known more for his ability to flatter and to excel at self-promotion than for his medical skills. He developed a large practice among people in the highest circles of society and reached the summit of his career in 1586 when he was made Physician-in-Chief to Queen Elizabeth I.

Lopez continued to be successful: he owned a house in Holborn and educated his son, Anthony, at Winchester College. He was viewed, outwardly at least, as a practising Protestant.

Treason and torture

On 1 January 1594, the Earl of Essex, accompanied by officers of the security forces, detained Lopez on suspicion of treason. They claimed they had discovered an elaborate plot to poison the Queen, to seize the English throne and to restore the Catholic religion. The plot was allegedly master-minded and financed by the Spanish government – and Lopez was to carry out the poisoning.

Lopez was imprisoned, interrogated and subjected to torture. When on the rack, he confessed he had accepted 50,000 crowns from Spanish intelligence services to carry out the deed. He later retracted the confession saying it was made under duress.

He was convicted in February but the Queen delayed signing the warrant for his execution as it is thought she felt he was innocent. Regardless, he was hanged, drawn and quartered on 7 June – but not before saying to the watching crowd that he loved the Queen as well as he loved Jesus Christ.

Lopez maintained his innocence to the end and

Portrait of Queen Elizabeth I attributed to George Gower

it has generally been agreed historically that he was innocent and that it was *known* he was innocent. Six months after his death the Crown restored Lopez's confiscated property to his wife and paid for his son Anthony's school fees (£30 a year) at Winchester.

PETER TURNER 1542–1614

Physician and Member of Parliament who sought to advance the Puritan cause

After leaving Bart's to become an MP, Peter Turner attempted to introduce legislation in support of a much more radical form of Protestantism than that favoured by Queen Elizabeth I.

The Elizabethan prayer book, which Turner wanted to replace

Peter Turner was the son of William Turner, a renowned botanist and influential churchman with strong anti-Catholic views. The Turner family fled England during the reign of the Catholic Queen Mary (1553–1558) but returned under Queen Elizabeth I, when William Turner became Dean of Wells. Peter thus grew up amid religious dissent and with a preference for a continental style of Protestantism.

Peter Turner began by studying both botany and medicine, but then decided on a career in medicine, going from Cambridge to Heidelberg to gain his MD. He was accepted as a Licentiate of the College of Physicians in 1582, after a dispute over his initial refusal to recognise the College's examination or pay the necessary fee to gain authorisation to practise in England. Presumably Bart's had been happy enough to accept Turner's German qualification as he was appointed physician there in 1581 to replace Roderigo Lopez.

Election to Parliament
Turner left Bart's in 1585, having become MP for Bridport, a seat he probably gained through the influence of titled Puritan sympathisers. He was soon appointed to the Committee for the Better Observing of the Sabbath Day. At this time, moderate Puritans were hoping to gain a measure of reform by presenting petitions to Parliament and these were being favourably received. The more radical Turner called for a 'bill and book' to be read which had been 'framed by certain

godly and learned' ministers. This would have replaced the Elizabethan prayer book and introduced a Presbyterian system of church government. Turner's motion was rejected. The following year a well organised group of radical Puritans enjoyed more support but this time Turner played only a minor role.

Turner spoke out in defence of radical Puritans imprisoned in the Tower of London and also joined in the outcry against the Catholic Mary Queen of Scots, demanding her execution and also stronger laws against the Papists who were plotting against Queen Elizabeth.

While an MP, Turner continued working as a physician and had a number of important patients, including Sir Walter Raleigh, whom he saw in the Tower. Peter Turner died on 27 May 1614 and was buried the next day in St Olave's, Hart Street.

LOST AND FOUND

Peter Turner's memorial statue was feared lost for ever after thieves stole it when St Olave's church was bombed in 1941. However, in 2010, the statue was recovered afer a Museum of London curator spotted its impending auction and told church officials. The statue is now back in its rightful place.

JOHN LYLY c.1553–1606

Wit, novelist, poet, playwright and politician

John Lyly was the most fashionable English writer of his day. His witty and astute sayings – reputedly including 'All's fair in love and war' – have been much quoted. He was buried in St Bartholomew the Less.

John Lyly was born in Kent, where his father, Peter Lyly, was Registrar to the Archbishop of Canterbury. His grandfather, William Lyly, was a noted grammarian. Aged 16, John became a student at Magdalen College, Oxford, where he received his bachelor's degree in 1573 and his master's in 1575. He then applied for a fellowship, but this was not granted. Lyly obviously had a good time at Oxford but it seems he never really took studying seriously, instead gaining a reputation as a 'noted wit'.

After university Lyly went to London and began his literary career. His first book, *Eupheus, the Anatomy of Wit*, was published in 1578, followed by *Eupheus and His England* in 1580. These early books were extremely popular and gave rise to the term 'Euphuism' to describe the elegant but high-flown style of writing he practised. Shortly afterwards, Lyly turned his attention to writing plays, which are still recognised today for their importance in the development of English drama. These included *Love's Metamorphosis, Sapho and Phao, Gallathea, Midas*, and *Endymion*, which were all in prose, and *The Woman in the Moon,* written in poetry. Lyly continued to enjoy considerable success, at least until the early 1590s. His plays were performed in front of Queen Elizabeth and also put on for a popular audience at the Blackfriars Theatre.

Blackfriars Theatre, where plays by Lyly were performed

From 1588 Lyly apparently held an honorary position at Court as Esquire of the Body to the Queen. However, it seems he was hoping for advancement. The position he really wanted was that of Master of Revels, but despite making two petitions to the Queen on this account, he was never to be given it by her.

Lyly married Beatrice Brown in 1583 and they had three children. While continuing to write, he sat in Parliament four times between 1589 and 1601. After 1592 his work steadily declined in influence and reputation, and he died poor and neglected early in the reign of King James I. Whether or not Lyly lived in the parish of St Bartholomew the Less is not documented but he was buried there on 20 November 1606.

TIMELESS SAYINGS FROM EUPHEUS

'Far more seemly to have thy study full of books, than thy purse full of money.'

•

'Love knoweth no laws.'

•

'In misery it is great comfort to have a companion.'

•

'Fish and guests in three days are stale.'

•

'As the best wine doth make the sharpest vinegar, so the deepest love turneth to the deadliest hate.'

•

'Delays breed dangers: nothing so perilous as procrastination.'

ANN BODLEY c.1564–1611

Wealthy wife whose money helped set up the Bodleian Library

Ann Bodley was a rich widow whose marriage to Sir Thomas Bodley enabled him to re-found the library at Oxford University. They lived in the parish of St Bartholomew's the Less and she is buried in the church.

The future Ann Bodley was the daughter of Richard Cary (or Carew), a rich Bristol merchant. Aged about 20, in 1584, she married Nicholas Ball, a wealthy pilchard merchant from Totnes, Devon, who was MP and then Mayor of the town. Their house in Totnes still stands. At least two children were born but the marriage was shortlived as Nicholas died in 1586. Ann became a very rich widow.

Still only 23, she married Thomas

Memorial stone in praise of Ann Bodley

Bodley, 20 years her senior, in 1587. Bodley was an Oxford University lecturer, an MP and a diplomat but today is best known for re-founding what would become the Bodleian Library. Ann's money would help restore the fabric and stock the library with books.

From 1599, the couple lived in the parish of St Bartholomew the Less, and on Ann's death, after 24 'sweet' years together, Thomas put up a memorial in the church praising her exemplary goodness.

THE CHURCH OF ST BARTHOLOMEW THE LESS

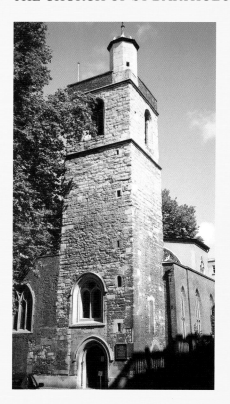

The site of the present church has been occupied since 1184. Although the hospital had other chapels in medieval times, this is the only survivor. When Henry VIII re-founded the hospital in 1546, its precinct was established as the Anglican parish of St Bartholomew the Less and it became unique among English hospitals as a parish in its own right. After the re-founding, there was a Vicar, who looked after the pastoral care of the parishioners, and a Hospitaller, who looked after the needs of the patients. These positions were combined in the 1600s.

Today, the oldest parts of the church are the 15th-century west wall and tower. The interior was rebuilt by George Dance in 1793, and then renovated in 1823 by Thomas Hardwick, who also took down much of the original church.

In the past, it was compulsory for nursing staff, and patients who were fit enough, to attend church services. In 1682 the governors were asked to check whether they and others were attending Communion according to the rites of the Church of England. The result was the dismissal of the brewer, baker, ironmonger, turner, mason, tinman, flaxman, mealman and stationer! Times have changed and there are now regular services for all denominations in this peaceful church.

INIGO JONES 1573–1652

Architect and designer responsible for introducing the Italian Renaissance style to England

Inigo Jones, who was christened in the church of St Bartholomew the Less, was considered to be the most talented artist in England in the first half of the 17th century.

Inigo Jones has an only tenuous but interesting link to St Bartholomew's Hospital. He was born in Smithfield, the son of a Welsh Catholic cloth worker, and was christened on 29 July 1573 in St Bartholomew the Less. It is possible that his family shifted its allegiance from the Catholic church to the Church of England for the sake of expediency.

Little is known about his early life other than he worked as an apprentice joiner in St Paul's churchyard and later became an architect. Among other artistic activities he designed costumes, drew scenery designs for masques, plays and other court entertainment, and probably introduced movable scenery and the proscenium arch to the English theatre.

Jones visited Italy frequently, which greatly influenced his classical style. His impressive work came to the notice of King James I who, in 1615, appointed him as chief architect to the Crown. Jones continued to hold this position under Charles I until 1642 at the start of the Civil War.

William Tite's painting combines several of Inigo Jones's important buildings

Theatrical costume design by Inigo Jones

Inigo Jones was the first professional architect in England in the modern sense of the term. It was Jones who took English architecture from its essentially medieval Gothic and Tudor traditions into the mainstream of the Italian Renaissance manner. The design of more than 120 buildings has been attributed to Jones.

His earliest surviving work is the Queen's House at Greenwich, started in 1616. The building most associated with Jones today is the Banqueting House at Whitehall, which was completed in 1622. In 1631 he designed London's first residential square in the style of an Italian Piazza, in Covent Garden. The design included terraced houses and the church of St Paul, which was London's first Anglican church to be built since the Reformation. Between 1634 and 1642 he extensively restored St Paul's Cathedral, sadly only for it to be destroyed in the Great Fire of London in 1666.

Inigo Jones's career effectively ended with the outbreak of the English Civil War when he was arrested and had his property seized for a year. He never married and, although christened in Bart's the Less, was buried with his parents in St Benet's, the Welsh church in the City of London.

WILLIAM HARVEY 1578–1657

Dapper little man who first described the circulation of the blood

In 1628 William Harvey told the scientific world about his great discovery: how the blood circulated round the body. By using methods of research that were quite different from those of his predecessors, he helped pave the way for a new generation of more scientific researchers.

The famous anatomical theatre at Padua, where William Harvey studied

William Harvey was the son of a well-to-do Kentish farmer. He was obviously a bright boy and after attending The King's School, Canterbury he was awarded a scholarship to Gonville and Caius College, Cambridge. Although he held the scholarship until 1599, he was absent for most of the last year having been severely ill with malaria.

After leaving Cambridge, Harvey continued his medical education in Italy, at the University of Padua, where he was fortunate to study under the famous pioneering anatomist and surgeon, Hieronymus Fabricius. Undoubtedly, Fabricius instilled in Harvey the importance of anatomy and gave him the thirst to carry out dissections. After gaining his diploma in 1602, at the age of 24, Harvey returned to England full of enthusiasm.

He became an established physician, but spent much of his time carrying out experiments on live animals so he could observe the beating of their hearts. He is known to have performed dissections on the bodies of executed criminals and it is even said that he dissected the bodies of his father and sister after their deaths.

Harvey was ambitious and his career was fortuitously helped by his marriage, in 1604, to Elizabeth Browne, the daughter of Lancelot Browne, who was physician to Queen Elizabeth I and King James I. Sadly, the couple had no children but for many years Elizabeth was devoted to her tame parrot. After its demise, Harvey, as might be expected, carried out a dissection on the parrot, only to find that the supposed male bird was, in fact, a female!

Move to Bart's

Harvey became a Fellow of the Royal College of Physicians in 1607 and at that time was one of only 40 qualified doctors in London. In 1609 he was appointed physician to St Bartholomew's Hospital, where he would normally have been expected to live in. However, Harvey was given permission to remain in his own house, near St Martin's Church off Ludgate Hill, as it was so near the hospital. When appointed, his annual salary was £25, which was raised in 1626 to £35.

At Bart's, Harvey was required to attend at least one day a week to see patients and at any other time if requested by the Matron. Ward visits were few and far between and he only saw patients on the ward if they were too ill to come to him. For those complaining of scurvy he ordered a mixture of scurvy grass (spoonwort), watercress, horseradish, pepper and nutmeg mixed in beer.

He was very small but obviously cut quite a dash, being described at the time as 'a man of lowest stature, round faced, with small very black eyes full of spirit and his hair as black as a raven and curling'. Apparently he was a 'swarthy and testy man who habitually wore a dagger'.

Lecturer, scientist and author

In 1615, while working at Bart's, Harvey was appointed by the Royal College of Physicians to deliver a series of prestigious annual lectures at the College, with the purpose of increasing the general knowledge of anatomy throughout England.

Harvey's unceasing interest in anatomical research, particularly with regard to the circulation of the blood, came to fruition in 1628 with the

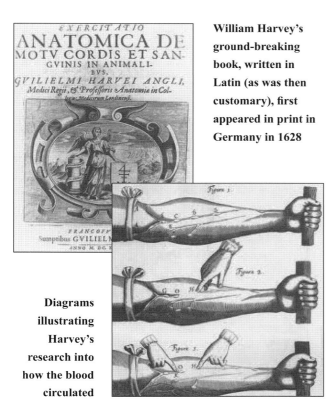

William Harvey's ground-breaking book, written in Latin (as was then customary), first appeared in print in Germany in 1628

Diagrams illustrating Harvey's research into how the blood circulated

publication in Frankfurt of his book *Anatomica De Motu Cordis et Sanguinis in Animalibus (Anatomy of the motion of the heart and blood in animals).* In it he presented and proved a radical new theory on how the blood moved round the body. He demonstrated that the heart was a pump forcing blood around the body in a circular course. Diagrams in the book show the experiments he made on veins to prove the presence of valves that ensure that the blood can flow only in one direction.

Although Harvey's claims were met with criticism and disbelief, he was sure he was right – and so he proved to be. After the publication of his book Harvey became more forthcoming about his other areas of research, including being the first to put forward the idea that humans and other mammals reproduced via the fertilisation of eggs by sperm.

Royal physician

Harvey became physician to King James I and later to Charles I, travelling with him to the Battle of Edgehill in 1642 during the Civil War. In 1643, Harvey was instructed to give up his post at Bart's

after being ordered to remain in attendance on the King at his headquarters in Oxford. He was made Warden of Merton College for a brief period and returned to London in 1646 when Oxford surrendered to Cromwell's army. Although heavily fined when the war was over, Harvey was not persecuted as a Royalist. He was though a broken man when the King was executed in 1649.

Harvey gradually retired from public life. In response to one of several attempts to bring him back into the working world, he said, 'Much better is it oftentimes to grow wise at home and in private, than by publishing what you have amassed with infinite labour. To stir up tempests that may rob you of peace for the rest of your days'.

William Harvey died in 1657, when he was 79, and left Bart's £30 in his will. His later years were saddened by ill health and by the destruction of a large part of his scientific papers by Parliamentary troops. His service to the King made him suspect in the eyes of Cromwell's government and, after 1643, his name is no longer mentioned in the hospital records. The governors of Bart's, keen Royalists themselves, had to be careful not to offend the new authorities. Harvey had served the hospital loyally for 35 years and, although much of his work was lost to posterity, nothing could dim the brilliance of his mind for scientific truth.

Harvey explaining his findings to King Charles I

MARGARET BLAGUE c.1605–1675

Matron of St Bartholomew's Hospital and heroine of the Great Plague

Mrs Margaret Blague was a surgeon's widow who, for 32 years (1643–1675), was the loyal and devoted Matron at Bart's. She steadfastly remained at her post during the Great Plague of London.

All we know about Margaret's early life is that her maiden name was Flint and she married William Blague, at St Martin, Ludgate on 14 October 1627. In that same year, her husband was admitted to the Company of Barbers and Surgeons.

In 1641, William died and Margaret was left with four children. It was not an easy time: the cost of living was rising, many people were without work and there was unrest on the streets of London. Fortunately, Margaret heard from her brother-in-law, who was Clerk to the Governors at Bart's, that the hospital needed a new Matron. Margaret applied at once and was appointed on 2 June 1643.

Her main duties included supervising 15 sisters, making sure they spent their spare time spinning or sewing, and supervising the hospital bed linen and blankets. Her annual salary was £33.2s.0d (rising in 1657 to £40), as well as her accommodation and the 'right to the profits of her cellar'. She earned the same as the Renter, more than the Clerk and the Steward – but half as much as the Cook!

Cavaliers and Roundheads facing up to fight

Bart's during the Civil War

The Civil War was a difficult time to be Matron. On one occasion, in 1647, the governors had to step in when one of the sisters withheld food from Parliamentarian soldiers, used abusive language toward them, and wished the head of General Fairfax 'upon London Bridge'. The sister was suspended but not dismissed because the hospital staff and governors sided mostly with the Royalists.

In 1650, a year after the execution of King Charles I, the hospital acquired an apparently unelected and uninvited new governor. This was Colonel Pride, a staunch supporter of Cromwell, whose disruptive actions included accusing the Treasurer and the Steward of the misappropriation of hospital funds.

Increased authority

In 1651 a committee met to review the rules of the hospital. The effect was to increase the Matron's responsibilities and to enhance her position. No sister could be appointed without Matron's prior approval. All nursing staff were expected to obey Matron and she had the authority to reprimand and even to dismiss them. She is known, for example, to have dismissed Jane Toppin, a sister who sold 'several potts of Phisick to strangers'. Others were reprimanded for drunkenness and for taking money from patients. The Matron could also dismiss patients if they became disorderly.

It became noticeable over the next ten years that comparatively few sisters misbehaved and patients' complaints against them faded out altogether. One more duty given to Mrs Blague by the committee was a strict order to see that the sisters and walking patients went to church every Sabbath Day and attended prayers on Thursdays and Saturdays.

Plague and Fire

When the plague began to spread in London in the late summer of 1665, the two physicians, Dr Micklethwaite and Dr Tearne, went to the country. Of the two surgeons, Henry Boone, 'desired to bee excused to doe the service' and Thomas Woodhall told the governors that 'the business was too hot for him'. A temporary surgeon was taken on. The Clerk, the Steward and the Renter remained in post along with Mrs Blague, her 15 sisters, an unknown number of nurses, and the apothecary Francis Bernard.

Margaret did her best to make the patients comfortable, preparing broth and warm drinks with her own hands 'to the great peril of her life'. The governors rewarded the faithful few who had carried on working with 'handsome sums of money'.

The Great Fire of 1666 did not quite reach the hospital but was a terrifying experience for all who saw the fire creeping near to the building.

There is no doubt that Margaret Blague was a remarkable woman. She was practical, intelligent and brave, and also clearly understood the need for discipline and training. She was Matron until the day she died, on 12 February 1675, and was buried in the church of St Bartholomew the Less.

Plague victims being carried away for mass burial

NURSING AT BART'S IN THE 16TH AND 17TH CENTURIES

Henry VIII's charter provided for 'one Matron and twelve women under her to make the beds and wash and attend upon' the patients. The first matron was Rose Fisher, who served from 1547 to 1559. There had been 'Sisters' at Bart's since medieval times. Only unmarried women and widows could be appointed. If they wanted to marry they were dismissed. Watchett blue cloth was introduced as the sisters' 'liveries' or uniform in 1554 and remained in use until the 1990s.

Each sister had charge of a ward and, apart from caring for the patients and giving them their 'meat and drink', much of her work was menial. She had to carry the soiled mattresses and dirty rushes from the ward floor to the sisters' garden to be burnt. She was responsible for fetching the coal and

A feeding horn

provisions, emptying the slops, and for the cleanliness of the ward. She washed the bed linen with wood-ash, pounding it in a big wooden vat (beating the buck). Free time was spent spinning flax. She had strict orders to avoid drunkenness and male company.

Sisters worked without staff until the arrival of 'Helpers' in 1647. The name 'Nurse' first appeared in the 1650s. From 1652 all new sisters had to have worked as a nurse or helper. Initially, the terms 'nurse' and 'helper' were interchangeable, but by the 1670s the status of helper was inferior to that of nurse.

There was much disorderly behaviour and drunkenness, and no retirement age. Even worse, most of the nurses had little education and lacked any kind of skill.

2

THE GEORGIAN ERA

During the 18th century the hospital was entirely rebuilt and all the medieval buildings disappeared. James Gibbs, the architect, planned the famous Square with its North, South, East and West wings, and William Hogarth painted the huge, impressive paintings that still adorn the Grand Staircase to the Great Hall.

Many famous Bart's surgeons served the population of London. John Freke did important work separating the surgeons from the barbers, and the flamboyant Percivall Pott was known for his bedside manner and his fractured leg. The bad tempered anatomist John Hunter studied at Bart's, while John Abernethy, perhaps the most famous surgeon of all, was well known for 'My Book' and for giving blunt advice. The surgeon Robert Knox got into a spot of bother by associating with the body snatchers Burke and Hare.

Among the intellectual physicians in this era was William Pitcairn who adopted his brother's nine children. Meanwhile, the War of American Independence provided an opportunity for a Bart's man to become a double agent. The energetic genius Thomas Young had a monument dedicated to him in Westminster Abbey, and the missionary Robert Morrison somewhat bizarrely wore a false pigtail.

Architect of the re-built Bart's, with the 'finest outdoor' room in England

James Gibbs was one of the most influential and outstanding architects of his day. He proved to be an excellent choice when the decaying old Bart's Hospital buildings were replaced in the 18th century. His harmonious 'Georgian' design had the magnificent and famous Square at its heart.

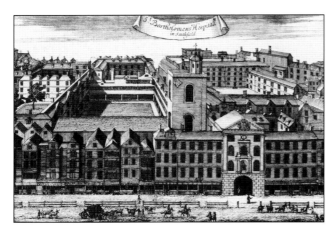

View of Bart's in 1720, showing the jumble of buildings that would be replaced when Gibbs's plans were implemented

James Gibbs was born in Scotland on 23 December 1682, to the merchant Patrick Gibbs and his second wife, Ann. James was educated at Aberdeen Grammar School and then at Marischal College in the same city. On the death of his parents, when he was 18, he went to stay with relatives in Holland and then travelled around Europe for several years before registering as a student at the Scots College in Rome, where he planned to study for the priesthood. Fortunately for St Bartholomew's Hospital, Gibbs had second thoughts and instead studied architecture under the famous Italian, Carlo Fontana. On completing his studies, he returned to London in 1708.

Architect in London
Gibbs was appointed architect in 1713 to the Commission for Building Fifty New Churches but was replaced in 1715, apparently due to the death of Queen Anne, the failure of the 1715 uprising, and the influence of the new Whig government. Gibbs himself was a Tory and also privately a Roman Catholic. Despite losing his position, Gibbs was

able to complete one church for the Commission in London: St Mary le Strand.

The breakthrough for Gibbs came in 1720 when he was invited to enter a competition to design a new church to replace the dilapidated church of St Martin-in-the-Fields – he won the competition and was appointed architect of the new church. After this success he became very famous and was described as 'the architect most in vogue'. He accepted a great many commissions and designed many important buildings, including the Radcliffe Camera in Oxford and Senate House in Cambridge. In 1723, Gibbs was rich enough to open an account at Drummonds Bank, where his first

The Square in the early 19th century, when an ugly pump at the centre somewhat spoilt the harmony of Gibbs's design

Architectural drawings of Gibbs's plans for the four new wings around a central square

year's balance amounted to £1055, 11 shillings and 4 pence.

The re-building of St Bartholomew's Hospital

The governors of Bart's first started discussing the possibility of re-building the decaying hospital in 1723, and that same year Gibbs was made a governor. A committee was appointed to draw up plans, the brief of which was to produce: 'a Plan for the re building of the hospital so the future buildings may be comfortable, to one Design and the whole process in time become more Regular and more useful'. Gibbs offered his services free of charge and the decision was made to accept his offer on 1 August 1728.

Grand Staircase in the North Wing

The initial scheme was not too ambitious and comprised a plan for the first of the new buildings to include a large hall for full meetings of the Board of Governors, several other rooms and a house for the Clerk. However, a few months later it was decided, due to the increasing population of the City, that all the wards should be pulled down and that all the 'buildings which shall be erected for the future shall be agreeable to one uniform plan'.

Gibbs produced a design for the new hospital with four detached wings round a central square. The South, West and East Wings were to contain the new wards, with each wing having 12 wards that could each accommodate 14 patients. The North Wing would be the administration block and would contain the Great Hall, the Clerk's house and other offices, and have a 'passage for coaches' running through its centre.

The Foundation Stone for the North Wing was laid on 9 July 1730 and this was the first block to be completed, in 1732. It was 40 years before all the building work was finished – with one interruption occurring in 1760 when the Treasurer, John Tuff, absconded to France with £4,094 in his pocket. The final transfer of patients, to the East Wing, took place in March 1769.

The Square

The approach to the Square remains today as it was intended by Gibbs all those years ago. It is entered through the archway under the North Wing. He left the central area of the Square empty in his original plan but this was occupied later by an ugly pump, which provided water to the wards. In 1859, the pump was replaced by the Fountain, which, since then, has been the focal point of the Square. For centuries, the Square has been the centre of life at Bart's and is remembered with nostalgia by all who have spent time at the hospital.

Other interests and personal life

James Gibbs was elected to the Royal Society in 1729 and over the years became a great book collector with wide interests. He was a man who enjoyed life, was fond of food and wine, and was described as 'corpulent'. He never married and died at his London house on the corner of Wimpole Street and Henrietta Place on 5 August 1754, aged 71.

Bart's Great Hall, the scene of many a grand occasion

JOHN FREKE 1688–1756

Pioneer ophthalmic surgeon influential in separating the professions of surgeon and barber

John Freke took up a unique position in 1727 when the governors of St Bartholomew's Hospital put him in charge of blind patients. Later in his career, he became a Serjeant-Surgeon to Queen Anne and played a prominent role in the establishment of the Company of Surgeons.

This splendid chandelier given to Bart's in 1735 has an inscription in Latin naming the donor as 'John Freke surgeon of this hospital'

John Freke, the son of a surgeon of the same name, was born in London in 1688. He was apprenticed to Mr Blundell whose daughter he later married.

In 1726, Freke was elected assistant surgeon to Bart's and almost immediately was appointed as the first curator of the hospital's museum. This was housed in a single room under the Cutting Ward and was grandly called 'a Repository for Anatomical and Chyrugical Preparations'. In fact, in its early days, the museum contained only stones removed by the surgeons, who had previously placed them in the Counting Room in readiness for patients to pay their bill. Later, after the Murder Act of 1752 had allowed the bodies of convicted murderers to be dissected for the study of anatomy, Freke was able to take advantage of a much better supply of specimens for the museum.

The first ophthalmic surgeon
In 1827 the governors at Bart's were beginning to realise the need for specialisation and it was recorded that 'through a tender regard for the deplorable state of blind people' they felt it 'proper to appoint Mr John Freke' to take care of the patients with diseases of the eyes.

Freke accepted the post and under instructions from the governors operated on the poor people who were considered fit enough for the operation. For each cataract 'couched' he was allowed to charge 6 shillings and 8 pence (the standard fee for all operations). This was a time when surgery was looked upon as being similar to a glorified haircut – and was charged accordingly.

Freke had a particularly good year in 1729, when he was elevated to the position of surgeon at Bart's and also elected a Fellow of the Royal Society. He became a governor of the hospital in 1736, a position he would hold until his death.

The Company of Surgeons
In December 1744 the surgical members of the Court of Assistants of the Company of Barbers and Surgeons, of which Freke was a member, submitted a proposal for separation. A committee of ten, consisting of an equal number of barbers and surgeons (including Freke) was appointed to report. In spite of opposition from the barbers, the surgeons petitioned Parliament for separation in January 1745 and the Royal Assent was granted within a few months. The Company of Surgeons was established, and surgery as a profession became fully recognised.

Freke became the third Master of the Company of Surgeons in 1747. However, it would seem that the new Company was for some years little more than a separation of Surgeons from Barbers. New Bye-laws for the Surgeons were approved in 1748 but were not printed until 1778. The Company was beset by financial and administrative problems, which were not easily overcome as the unbusinesslike surgeons acted like prima donnas.

Diverse interests

John Freke was a man with many interests, both medical and outside medicine. Over the years he designed several medical instruments, including improved obstetric forceps and an instrument for reducing dislocations of the shoulder.

In 1748, he published *An Essay on the Art of Healing,* in which he endeavoured to explain 'pus laudabile, or matter, and also incarning and cicatrising, and the causes of various diseases'. In this

In Hogarth's 'The Reward of Cruelty' Freke is seen in the role of Master

name by Henry Fielding in his book *Tom Jones.* Among Freke's other interests were art and music. He was a friend of William Hogarth, whose work he preferred to that of court painter Anthony van Dyck. John Freke is believed to have been the model for the Master of the Company of Surgeons in *The Reward of Cruelty.* This last plate of Hogarth's 1751 series *The Four Stages of Cruelty* depicts the fate of the cruel villain – to be dissected for anatomical research.

work Freke recommended early paracentesis in the treatment of empyema, and also identified the danger of not removing infected lymphatic tissue in those with cancer.

Freke was also known for his interest in other scientific subjects. He performed experiments with electricity and published books on the subject, including *An Essay to show the Cause of Electricity and why some things are Non-Electricable*, published in 1748, and *A Treatise on the Nature and Property of Fire*, published in 1752. It would appear that many of his ideas were more interesting on account of their originality than for their accuracy. He believed, for example, that electricity attracted pollen from one plant to another, and that electricity was the cause of acute rheumatism. As a result of his interest in electricity, Freke was mentioned by

Retirement and death

Freke held his position as surgeon until 1755, when gout and infirmity compelled him to resign. On his retirement he presented the hospital with an impressive gilded wood chandelier, which still hangs today in the hallway of the Grand Staircase leading up to the Great Hall.

John Freke died on 7 November 1756, some 15 years after his wife, Elizabeth. On her death, he had obtained formal permission from the governors to bury her in the church of St Bartholomew the Less. He also requested that when he died, he too would be buried there. His wishes were honoured and he was entombed beside his wife under the canopy of a 15th-century tomb.

WILLIAM HOGARTH 1697–1764

Famous artist whose dramatic paintings for Bart's took the art world by surprise

William Hogarth is most generally known as the father of English satirical caricature. However, anyone who has ever visited the Great Hall at St Bartholomew's Hospital will also remember him for his depictions of care and healing in the two large dramatic paintings that adorn the staircase.

William Hogarth, the son of Richard Hogarth and Anne Gibbons, was born on 19 November 1697. As a child, William lived at 58 Bartholomew Close, where he was surrounded by the seamier side of Smithfield life. His father, a Latin teacher and textbook writer, had mixed fortunes, including five years in Fleet Prison for debt due to the failure of the Latin-speaking coffee house he had opened.

When William Hogarth was 16 he was apprenticed to Ellis Gamble, a silver plate engraver, and there learned to engrave trade cards and similar products. By 1720 Hogarth had his own business engraving book plates and painting portraits. At this time Hogarth was very impressed by the history paintings of Sir James Thornhill and made regular visits to Thornhill's free academy in Covent Garden. The two men became close friends and in 1729 Hogarth married Thornhill's daughter Jane. The couple were childless but by all accounts were fond of children as they fostered foundling children and Hogarth would later become a founding governor of London's Foundling Hospital.

Orgy scene from Hogarth's 'A Rake's Progress'

Satirical and moral works

During the 1720s, Hogarth worked for the print seller Philip Overton and started to produce political satires. These were well received and included, in 1726, *The Punishment Inflicted on Lemuel Gulliver,* a satire on the then Prime Minister, Robert Walpole.

Hogarth also became known at this time for producing works on what were described as 'modern moral subjects'. They included several important series of paintings and etchings presented in a form similar to a comic strip. Many of the characters who appeared in them had been observed and drawn from life by Hogarth, who always enjoyed the busy street life and fairs of the metropolis. The first of Hogarth's great moral series, *A Harlot's Progress*, was published in 1731–1732.

By the 1730s Hogarth was an established artist with an extensive portfolio, but he suffered financially from print sellers who reproduced his work without paying royalties. To tackle this problem, Hogarth managed to persuade his friends in Parliament to pass the Engravers' Copyright Act of 1735 and later that year he established St Martin's Lane Academy, a guild for professional artists and a school for young artists.

The Staircase paintings

Hogarth had a particular fondness for Bart's. Not only was it next door to his birthplace, and therefore his local hospital, but he had been baptised in the church of St Bartholomew the Great.

When he heard that the governors had decided to build a new North Wing at the hospital in the 1730s and that they wanted a spectacular entrance with a grand staircase on which huge historical paintings were to be hung, Hogarth offered his services free of charge. The offer was gratefully accepted, even though the governors had originally planned to

'Christ at the Pool of Bethesda' - allegedly with Bart's patients as models

employ the Venetian artist Jacopo Amigoni. Always insecure about his own social status, Hogarth had two motives for wanting to fulfil the commission: he wanted to make a generous offer to the hospital which would make him look good but he also wanted to demonstrate that an English artist could excel at the grand historical style of painting.

The Bart's paintings were begun around 1734 and were undoubtedly a very different challenge for Hogarth as he was not used to painting in the classical style. *The Good Samaritan* depicts a traveller who, after being been beaten and robbed, is saved not by two holy men, who pass him by, but by a Samaritan, from a despised race, who stopped and cared for him. *Christ at the Pool of Bethesda* is an enormous painting, thirty feet across, showing the biblical scene of Christ healing a man who has been unable to walk for many years. Tradition has it that in the *Bethesda* picture Hogarth used patients from the wards at Bart's both as models and also as a teaching aid for the trainee physicians so they could endeavour to diagnose the various conditions of those depicted.

Although *Christ at the Pool of Bethesda* was painted on canvas and then transported from a studio in St Martin's Lane before being erected on the staircase, *The Good Samaritan* was painted

on site with Hogarth perched on scaffolding. It is thought that although he painted all the figures, some of his artist friends helped with the landscape, decorative borders and scrollwork.

The grand unveiling of the paintings took place in 1737 and took the art world by surprise. Many considered that although the people in the paintings showed interesting qualities, such as 'human drama and pitiful ironies', they were 'out of place in the idealised landscape that suited the tastes of our continental cousins'. Disappointingly for Hogarth, few other commissions for similar pictures came his way and he returned to depicting modern morality tales, such as *Gin Lane*, an 18th-century take on the evils of binge drinking.

William Hogarth became a governor at Bart's in recompense for his paintings. At the time it was customary for those who donated £50 or more to be rewarded by being made a governor. In Hogarth's case the donation was his art not his money. Happily his mother still lived nearby when the paintings were installed in the new building – and no doubt she was very proud. It was a symbol of how far he had come.

Hogarth died on 25 October 1764 and was buried in St Nicholas Churchyard, Chiswick, London.

Hogarth's ' The Good Samaritan' painted in situ at Bart's

WILLIAM PITCAIRN 1711–1791

President of the Royal College of Physicians for ten consecutive years

William Pitcairn played a significant role at the Royal College of Physicians as well as being a dedicated Bart's man and a remarkable uncle.

Born in Dysart, Fife in 1711, William Pitcairn was the son of the Rev. David Pitcairn and Catherine Hamilton. Both his parents came from well-connected gentry families and his mother was reputed to be a descendant of Robert the Bruce.

As a young man, William left Scotland to study medicine at Leiden in the Netherlands before moving to Rheims in France where he received his MD degree. Pitcairn then spent time in Oxford,

The Radcliffe Camera, where Pitcairn received his degree

where he stayed with and tutored his mother's cousin, the 6th Duke of Hamilton. In 1749, at a ceremony in the newly opened Radcliffe Camera, he received the degree of doctor of medicine by diploma from Oxford University. The following year, aged 37, Pitcairn began practising in London, where he settled easily into the capital city's flourishing intellectual community.

Royal College of Physicians

The Royal College of Physicians admitted William Pitcairn as a candidate in 1749 and he quickly achieved eminence with both the profession and the public. He gave the prestigious Goulstonian Lecture in 1752 and was appointed Censor several times before being elected President of the College in ten consecutive years from 1775. On his retirement he was thanked for 'his unremitting attention to the affairs of the College and for the great zeal which he showed for its honour and prosperity'.

Physician, Almoner and Treasurer at Bart's

Pitcairn was elected physician to Bart's in 1750 and continued working there for the next 30 years. He was admitted a Fellow of the Royal Society and was well known as a sound and successful physician who introduced and taught a much freer use of opium in the treatment of disease and fevers. When he retired, in 1780, Pitcairn gave £100 to the hospital, and the governors expressed their thanks for his 'care, attention and humanity to the poor'.

In 1782, to mark the value of his services to Bart's, the governors invited Pitcairn to become an Almoner (one of four governors with day-to-day duties). He was subsequently appointed Treasurer to the hospital in 1784.

The family man

William Pitcairn was apparently an attractive and active man and it is perhaps surprising that

Pitcairn island (1 mile by 2) named for William's nephew

he seems never to have married. He was, though, very close to his family, and when his favourite brother, John, died a hero in 1775 during the American Revolution, William adopted and supported John's nine children. Among them were David Pitcairn, who was to succeed his uncle at Bart's, and Robert, who, as a midshipman in 1767, was the first to sight Pitcairn Island in the Pacific Ocean.

William Pitcairn was an expert botanist, and at his home in Islington he had a botanical garden abundantly stocked with scarce and valuable plants. It was there that he died on 25 November 1791. He was buried on 1 December 1791 in a vault in the church of St Bartholomew the Less.

THE ROYAL COLLEGE OF PHYSICIANS:
THE OLDEST MEDICAL COLLEGE IN ENGLAND

Early in the 16th century, the elite, educated physicians in London felt they should have the power to grant licences exclusively to those they considered qualified to practise medicine. They also sought to punish unqualified practitioners and those engaged in malpractice. A small group, led by Thomas Linacre, therefore made plans to found an academic college for physicians; they wanted to demonstrate that a degree and an oral examination were required for physicians and that a classical education was as important as medical knowledge.

In 1518, in response to a petition, King Henry VIII granted a royal charter to the College of Physicians. The founding charter decreed that the college would 'curb the audacity of those wicked men who shall profess medicine more for the sake of their avarice than from the assurance of any good conscience'. In 1523 an Act of Parliament extended the College's licensing powers from London to the whole of England. However, it was not until after 1660 and the restoration of the monarchy that the College became consistently known as the Royal College of Physicians.

Struggles for acceptance

The newly established College faced immediate problems with other medical bodies in the struggle to control medical licensing, and resistance to College control persisted. Until the 19th century there were usually fewer than 60 fellows at any one time and under 100 members with degrees. In 1767, the College became involved in a bitter dispute with its own licentiates when they refused to admit candidates for Fellowship from non-Oxbridge universities. It was to take until 1835 for candidates from other universities to be finally admitted as Fellows and given full voting rights. Women were to wait still longer. They were completely excluded from entry until 1909 and it was not until 1934 that the first female Fellow was elected.

To the present day

Over the centuries, numerous Bart's physicians have served the College, many in senior positions. William Pitcairn was certainly one who was totally committed to its cause, as was Norman Moore, President from 1918 to 1921. Today, the College continues to hold membership examinations and to elect Fellows from the general membership.

THE GOLD-HEADED CANE

This splendid gold-headed cane was presented to the Royal College of Physicians in 1835 by the widow of Matthew Baillie. It had been carried first by Dr John Radcliffe (1650-1714), and then handed down to and carried over more than a century by four other eminent physicians: Richard Mead, Anthony Askew, William Pitcairn and Matthew Baillie.

PERCIVALL POTT 1714–1788

Humane surgeon in the days before anaesthesia

Percivall Pott was a Bart's man through and through, who cut a stylish figure with his plum velvet coat, lace ruffles, knee britches and sword. He was dedicated to his patients and is well known today for several conditions that bear his name.

A familiar scene for Pott who spent over 50 years at Bart's

Percivall Pott was born in Threadneedle Street on 6 January 1714. His father, also called Percivall, was a notary of well-known Cheshire lineage, who died when young Percivall was only four years old. His mother came from a family who ran an old-established City firm and had links to the founders of the Bank of England. It is thought that because Percivall Pott the surgeon came from a better background than most of his peers, he helped to raise the social status of surgeons in England.

The young Percivall was supported by the Bishop of Rochester, a distant relative, who paid for his education. As a boy, Percivall planned to be a clergyman but changed his mind aged 15, when he was apprenticed for £200 to Edward Nourse, a surgeon from Bart's. One of Pott's duties during his seven-year apprenticeship as Nourse's primary assistant was to dissect and prepare cadavers for anatomy demonstrations, which were performed at Nourse's house in Aldersgate Street.

Surgeon at Bart's

Pott built up a good professional reputation and in 1736, aged 22, he received the freedom of the Company of Barbers and Surgeons and was awarded an honorary Grand Diploma in recognition of his exceptional surgical skills.

Pott was appointed assistant surgeon to Bart's in 1745, the same year that he took an active part in the separation of the Surgeons from the Barbers to form separate companies. From then on he played a major role in the organisational affairs of the Company of Surgeons – the forerunner of the Royal College of Surgeons of England – and was elected one of the first masters of anatomy. Later, in 1765, he would be made Governor of the Company, after his election as a member of the Royal Society the previous year.

After four years as an assistant, Pott was appointed a full surgeon at Bart's in 1749. He attracted many foreign students and also had a thriving private practice. He was extraordinarily busy and became one of the most famous English surgeons of the mid 18th century. His patients included David Garrick, Thomas Gainsborough and Samuel Johnson.

Pott actively sought ways of performing operations in as humane a way as possible. This was in the days before anaesthesia, when patients requiring surgery often found that the 'cure' was worse than the disease itself. Pott avoided using cautery wherever possible, as the hot metal instruments that were used to burn tissue to stop bleeding caused not only pain but also extensive tissue damage. He became renowned

---

EPONYMS FOR PERCIVALL POTT

- Pott's aneurysm
- Pott's cancer
- Pott's disease
- Pott's fracture
- Pott's gangrene
- Pott's paraplegia
- Pott's puffy tumour

for being very concerned with the basic comfort of his patients, on the wards at Bart's and in his private practice.

The riding accident

In 1756, when Pott was 42, he became a patient himself after falling from his horse on his way to visit a patient in the Old Kent Road. He sustained a bad fracture of the leg (sometimes confused with the fractured dislocation of the ankle later described by him and which is still known as Pott's fracture).

Pott refused to be moved and sent for a door to

Portrait of Percivall Pott displayed at the Royal College of Surgeons

which two poles were nailed in order to form an improvised stretcher on which he could be carried home. A group of surgeons, with Pott, decided the way forward was amputation of the limb. However, as the instruments were being prepared, Edward Nourse arrived and made the decision to try and save the leg by placing it in a splint. This was a major advance in the treatment of fractures, and after a time the injury healed satisfactorily.

The enforced rest after his accident allowed Pott to embark on his writing career. He published a series of pamphlets on a variety of conditions, including *Fractures and Dislocations* and *A Treatise on Ruptures* – he was indeed a generalist!

Pott also began lecturing and proved to be lively, interesting and above all practical. He considered that surgical books were all very well in terms of theory but of most value was teaching by the bedside, when he always urged his students to put dexterity before mere speed.

Chimney-sweep's cancer

In 1775 Pott reported the first occupational cancer. He noticed a curious prevalence of ragged sores on

Falling from a horse gave Pott a serious leg fracture

the scrotums of many chimney sweeps in London. He realised, unlike some of his colleagues who thought the men were afflicted with a venereal disease, that the men were suffering from a type of skin cancer caused by a 'lodgement of soot in the rugae' of the scrotum. These men were continually exposed to coal tar and were 'perculiarly liable' to this form of cancer. Pott's observation was a medical milestone and documented for the first time that cancer could be caused by an external agent rather than by internal factors. Other disorders he described and which bear his name include Pott's puffy tumour and Pott's paralysis.

Percivall Pott remained at Bart's until 1787, having served the institution 'as a man and boy' for half a century. He continued seeing his private patients until, on 11 December 1788, he returned from visiting a patient some 20 miles from London having caught a cold. The next day he was persuaded by his son-in-law, also a medical man, to let him do his calls. Pott agreed to this but also ventured out himself to make a sick round of London. His condition deteriorated and on 21 December he made his last diagnosis: 'My lamp is almost extinguished: I hope it has burned for the benefit of others'. The next day he died of pneumonia.

JOHN HUNTER 1728–1793

Maverick surgeon who enjoyed working with the dead as much as the living

John Hunter is considered to be the father of scientific surgery in the United Kingdom. He was a talented anatomist, dissector and observer who was revered and feared in equal measure.

Early portrait of John Hunter, surgeon and scientist

John Hunter was born in Scotland on 13 February 1728. He was the youngest of ten children and spent many happy hours exploring the countryside and enjoying the wildlife but did not receive much formal education and was slow to learn. When he was twenty he made his way to London on horseback to join his brother William, who was ten years older, as his assistant anatomist.

John became a brilliant dissector and anatomist and was keen to work with body snatchers, often referred to as 'resurrectionists'. During twelve years of working with William, John admitted to being present at the dissection of more than two thousand bodies. It was also during this period that he began his obsessive collection of animals and plants on which to experiment and which would later provide the material for his teaching museum.

The surgeon

From 1752 to 1753 Hunter studied at Bart's under Percivall Pott, whom he much admired. While there he treated his earliest recorded patient – a sweep with gonorrhoea who had developed a stricture of his urethra. After trying a traditional method of treatment, which was unsuccessful, Hunter tried an experimental procedure, which cured the patient.

His approach was 'first try traditional, analyse the outcome, form a hypothesis aimed at improvement and implement the results'. This became his standard practice and was the foundation for the scientific revolution of surgery.

Hunter also studied at this time under William Cheselden, at Chelsea Hospital and St George's Hospital, as well as attending St Mary's Hall, Oxford in 1755 as a gentleman commoner. In 1756 he was made assistant house surgeon at St George's and there discovered placental circulation.

When George III became King in 1760, Hunter was 33 years old and still had no formal qualification or permanent job. He decided to join the army and served as a staff surgeon on active service for the last three years of the Seven Years War. He became an expert on gunshot wounds and showed that many amputations could be avoided if the wound was treated properly. This resulted in the publication of his *A Treatise on the Blood, Inflammation and Gunshot Wounds* (1794).

On leaving the army, in 1763, Hunter formed a partnership with the dentist James Spence, and to supplement his income he set up his own private anatomy school. Hunter was at last becoming recognised and, in 1767, he was elected Fellow of the Royal Society. In 1768 he became a member of the Company of Surgeons (with Pott as an examiner), and was appointed surgeon at St George's Hospital.

Hunterian Society Medal, still awarded today

Hunter was keen to follow in Pott's footsteps by giving lectures free of charge to the pupils at St George's. (At this time, Bart's was the only one of London's six general hospitals that provided lectures.) However, Hunter's request, was turned down, and he became – and remained – unpopular with his colleagues.

Pre-eminence and fame

John Hunter's next few years were extraordinarily fruitful. Not only did he marry the beautiful and clever Ann Home and father four children (two of whom died in infancy), but he became, apart from Pott, the most fashionable surgeon in England. He was appointed Surgeon Extraordinary to the King; he was consulted by Benjamin Franklin; he carried out a post mortem on Prime Minister Rockingham; he operated on young William Pitt (who was very brave); and he embalmed George III's aunt, Princess Amelia. His portrait was painted by Joshua Reynolds and hung in the Royal Academy, and when Reynolds died some years later, Hunter conducted the autopsy. Hunter also continued with his writing (although he was always careful to get others to check his spelling and punctuation) and opened the museum at his home for viewing twice a year.

In 1790, Hunter invented a method of artificial feeding, and also that year was appointed Surgeon General to the British Army. The following year, he helped found the Veterinary College of London. Hunter was now in his sixties but refused to slow down in spite of suffering from attacks of angina. On 13 February 1793, during a stormy meeting at St George's Hospital, Hunter was, as usual, speaking his mind and was unable to contain his

Hunter's impressive collection on display at the RCS

temper. He suddenly collapsed into the arms of one of the physicians and died. In accordance with his instructions, his body was dissected by his brother-in-law, Everard Home.

Six years later, in 1799, Pitt's government agreed to buy Hunter's museum, which held more than 13,000 preparations, and gave custody of it to the Company of Surgeons. Unfortunately, Hunter's papers had been burned by Everard Home. John Hunter was reinterred on 28 March 1859 in Westminster Abbey.

CHARLES BYRNE, IRISH GIANT

Charles Byrne, a well-known giant, was reputed to be 8ft 4in tall. Fearing that anatomists might want to dissect his body, Byrne requested that on his death his remains be thrown deep into the sea.

When Byrne died, aged 22, John Hunter paid the undertaker £500 to procure the cadaver. Byrne's friends kept watch over the body but, on stopping off for refreshment on their way to Margate, they put the coffin in a neighbouring barn. There, the undertakers' accomplices unscrewed the lid of the coffin and swapped the corpse for paving stones. The unsuspecting mourning party then plunged the stone-filled coffin into the sea.

Byrne's body was meanwhile hidden under straw in a cart and delivered to Hunter, who immediately chopped up the cadaver and boiled the pieces in a large vat. The bones were then painstakingly reassembled to make Byrne's skeleton.

Hunter told not a soul for four years. Today, Charles Byrne's skeleton resides in the Hunterian Museum at the Royal College of Surgeons.

EDWARD BANCROFT 1744–1821

American-born physician, scientist and double agent during the American War of Independence

Edward Bancroft was a man who lived for the main chance. He left the Americas to advance his career in London, where his apprenticeship at St Bartholomew's Hospital gave him the opportunity to practise medicine while embarking on other more sinister pursuits.

Edward Bancroft was born and raised in colonial America. His father died when he was two and a major influence in his teens was his schoolmaster, Silas Deane, who would also figure later in his life.

Edward began work as a medical apprentice in Connecticut. He then spent time in Guiana before arriving in London in 1767 to further his medical training at Bart's. During this period the hospital attracted three types of student – physicians in practice, those who were proceeding to medical degrees, and apprentices. Bancroft fell into the third category and is likely to have been apprenticed to William Pitcairn, to whom he dedicated *An Essay on the Natural History of Guiana in South America,* published in 1769. He was elected a Fellow of the Royal Society in 1773, and in 1774 obtained his MD from Aberdeen, without visiting the university.

Double agent

One of Bancroft's friends in London was Benjamin Franklin, the American philosopher, diplomat and colonial agent. In 1776, Franklin, a supporter of American independence, suggested that Silas Deane, now working for the American cause in Paris, should recruit Bancroft as a spy for the colonies.

Despite promising to help Deane, Bancroft did not want America to become independent and, after meeting with the British Secret Service chief, he agreed to become a double agent. Fortuitously, Franklin now appointed Bancroft as secretary to the American Commission in Paris. This enabled Bancroft to send reports to the British, which he wrote in a special invisible ink between the lines of weekly 'chatty' letters. The reports were put in a bottle left in a hole in a tree for collection by a British official who replaced them with new orders. Through this method, George III apparently saw the 1778 American Treaty of Alliance with France two days after it was signed.

The Americans in Paris were aware there was a spy in their midst but nothing was proven. It has, though, been suggested that before Deane could return to America in 1789 and expose Bancroft's double dealings, he was poisoned by Bancroft who gave him a large dose of laudanum. Bancroft's activity as a double agent remained hidden until 1889, when British diplomatic papers were disclosed to the public. They included a letter, from 1784, in which Bancroft pressed for the reinstatement of his pension for services rendered, denied any engagement with any government in the USA, and pledged his loyalty to the King.

After the war, Bancroft lived in England and became wealthy as a dye importer. His *Experimental Researches Concerning Permanent Colors* was well received and in 1797 he was elected a member of the American Academy of Arts and Sciences.

Lexington, 1775, at the start of the American War of Independence

JOSEPH ADAMS 1756–1818

Apothecary turned physician, advocate of vaccination for smallpox and researcher into hereditary diseases

Joseph Adams was an early advocate of smallpox vaccination. He was also the author of a remarkable clinical study of hereditary diseases – a work that was not taken seriously by his contemporaries but which has been validated by the work of 20th century geneticists.

Joseph Adams, the son of a religious dissenter, was not allowed to study for an English medical degree because only practising Anglicans could attend Oxford and Cambridge at this time – and no other university courses were available. Instead, Joseph became apprenticed to his father, a London apothecary. In this role he carried out hospital duties and studied at Bart's (under Pitcairn and Pott), at Guy's, and at St George's (under John Hunter).

Surgeon and physician

Continuing to work as an apothecary, Adams became a member of the Corporation of Surgeons in 1790. Then, in 1796, he was awarded an MD by Aberdeen University after publishing a small volume on *Morbid Poisons*. Ready for a change of scene, Adams left London for Madeira, where he spent the next eight years practising medicine and researching

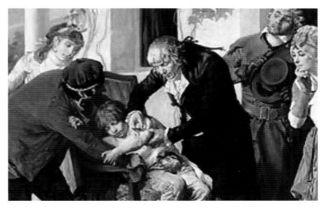

The first smallpox vaccination was given by Jenner in 1796

into smallpox and other diseases.

On his return to England Adams was admitted to the London Royal College of Physicians, and rules were bent to allow him to become physician at the Smallpox Hospital. He was a strong advocate of vaccination against smallpox, believing like Edward Jenner (who discovered the vaccine) that cowpox was just a weak version of smallpox.

Study of hereditary diseases

Joseph Adams came into his own when in 1814 he wrote *A Treatise on the Supposed Hereditary Properties of Diseases*. Adams approached the topic from his own clinical experience and observations, and his book was probably the first to attempt to clarify the nature, meaning and origins of hereditary traits. He even discussed 'survival of the fittest' – 45 years before Darwin's book was published. Sadly, Adams's ideas, for which he could offer no scientific basis, were largely ignored by his contemporaries.

Adams was 62 when he died. He was well regarded but thought by some to have been too ambitious and overly sensitive to criticism – perhaps because his initial lack of a medical degree made him something of an outsider.

APOTHECARIES

In the 18th century, most people's medical care continued to be provided by apothecaries, whose job was to prepare and sell medicines. Many, however, had previously flouted the law by dispensing their remedies without a doctor's prescription. In 1704, an apothecary, William Rose, won an appeal in the House of Lords against the College of Physicians – which, as the authority for medical practice, had sought to limit the apothecary's role. By allowing apothecaries to prescribe and dispense, this ruling led to the evolution of the apothecary into today's general practitioner of medicine.

JOHN ABERNETHY 1764–1831

Charismatic and eccentric surgeon, founder of Bart's Medical College and the Museum of Pathology

John Abernethy became one of the most famous surgeons of his day – not because he was outstanding with the knife but because of his power of oratory and his immensely popular publication known as 'My Book'.

John Abernethy was only a lad of fifteen when he was apprenticed to the Bart's assistant surgeon Charles Blicke. By all accounts John was a dedicated student and attended many lectures by the eminent surgeons Percivall Pott and John Hunter. Hearing them may have inspired him to follow in their footsteps, as he also started delivering lectures – on anatomy and physiology as well as pathology and surgery – following his own promotion to assistant surgeon.

In the beginning, Abernethy held his lectures in his house in Bartholomew Close. However, they became so popular that they were soon over-subscribed, not only by Bart's students but also by those from other hospitals. Before long the venue was too small to accommodate everyone. Fortunately, the governors at Bart's came to the rescue and ordered the building of a new lecture theatre, at an estimated cost of £875. This was up and running by 1795 and came to be known both as the 'Surgeons Theatre' and the 'Medical Theatre'.

Due largely to Abernethy's popularity, his amusing anecdotes and his superb teaching skills, the new lecture theatre was found in its turn to be too small.

> ### A PROPOSAL OF MARRIAGE
>
> *'I have witnessed your devotion and kindness to your mother. I am in need of a wife, and I think you are the very person that would suit me. My time is incessantly occupied and I have therefore no leisure for courting. Reflect on this matter until Monday.'* She did – and she accepted.

By 1820 the charismatic Abernethy was frequently lecturing to several hundred surgical students. Once again the governors were prevailed upon for funding but this time they were reluctant to give any money because the first theatre had cost twice the amount estimated and the overspend had never been approved.

Important developments

Abernethy possessed great powers of persuasion but the deciding factor in the discussions was most probably inter-hospital rivalry (which was firmly in place even in those days). The governors gave their agreement to the plans for the new larger theatre after the Treasurer and Almoner visited St Thomas's and Guy's hospitals and found that Bart's was lagging behind as both of them could already accommodate large numbers of listeners at lectures. The new Bart's lecture theatre was opened in 1822, when 406 people attended Abernethy's first lecture there.

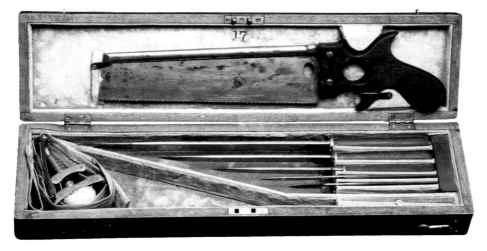

Case of John Abernethy's amputation instruments now in the Bart's Museum

---

SOME BLUNT ADVICE FOR PATIENTS

To the mother of a girl in tightly laced stays:
'Why, Madam, do you know there are upward of thirty yards of bowels squeezed underneath that girdle of your daughter's? Go home and cut it: let nature have fair play, and you will have no need of my advice.'

To a lazy patient asking how to cure gout:
'Live upon a sixpence a day – and earn it.'

To a patient who complained of pain when he moved his arm in a particular way:
'Well what a fool you must be to do it then.'

The opening of this new lecture theatre is considered to be the beginning of the medical school at Bart's, and John Abernethy is recognised as its founder. In addition to giving his own very popular lectures, Abernethy coordinated lectures that had previously been given by private individuals into a structured course, which became the basis of the Medical College in 1843.

Abernethy is also credited with the establishment of the hospital's museum of pathological anatomy. Although the museum building was not built until the 1870s, Abernethy was a strong advocate for the collection of pathological specimens for research and educational purposes.

Abernethy's Book

John Abernethy published a book in 1805 in which he put forward his theories. Its title was *Surgical Observations on the Constitutional Origins and Treatment of Local Diseases* but he always spoke of it as *'My Book'*. He referred to it in every lecture and apparently to every patient, telling them to take note of page 72 which advised that 'local diseases which are not the immediate consequence of accidental injury are the results of disorders of the digestive organs, and are all to be cured by attention to the

diet, by small doses of mercury, and by purgatives'. This recommendation suited the well-fed and free-living Londoners who crowded his waiting room where he gave his blunt advice.

He was not known for good manners and is said to have stood with his hands in his breeches even when addressing royalty. Nursing staff did not escape his rude manner and, suspecting a corpulent Bart's ward sister to be an alcoholic, he is reputed to have poked her midriff with a cane, saying, 'If that's not a bottle of gin ma'am I'll beg your pardon'. He was right – there was a resounding crashing of broken glass and a smell of gin soaking her dress!

George Macilwain wrote of Abernethy that, 'though not a little remarkable for his eccentricities of his manner, and an affected roughness in his intercourse with his ordinary patients, he was generally very kind and courteous in those cases which required the full exercise of his skill and knowledge'.

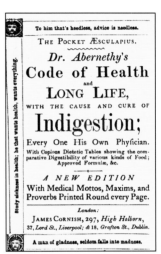

A small volume of 1856, based on 'My Book'

John Abernethy resigned his appointment as full surgeon at St Bartholomew's Hospital in 1827 and died, after a lingering illness, in April 1831, aged 67.

THE ABERNETHY BISCUIT

Abernethy's biscuit was an adaptation of the naval plain biscuit (hard tack). The doctor's medicinal, and more palatable, recipe added sugar for energy and caraway seeds to aid the digestion.

THOMAS YOUNG 1773–1829

Eminent polymath who deserves to be better remembered

Thomas Young was probably the most learned, profound and variously accomplished scholar and man of science to have lived in the early 19th century. Surprisingly, he slipped into obscurity.

Thomas Young was a child prodigy born to Quaker parents. By the age of four he had read the whole bible, and at 14 had mastered the classics, gained a good understanding of Italian, German, Arabic and Hebrew, and read avidly on natural sciences.

In 1791 he arrived at Bart's to study medicine and anatomy. During this time, at the young age of 21, he was elected to a Fellowship of the Royal Society for his work on the mechanics of accommodation of focus in the human eye. John Hunter immediately claimed the discovery, but Young was acquitted of plagiarism. In 1794 Thomas Young moved to Edinburgh, before going to Germany a year later, where he obtained the degree of doctor of physics.

Back from Germany, Young entered Emmanuel College, Cambridge in 1797. While there, he enjoyed private dancing lessons, learning the flute, horse riding and theatre going, but was formally disowned by the Quakers in 1798 as it was reported that he had 'attended places of public diversion'.

Physician, scientist and scholar

After two years at Cambridge, Young became established as a physician at 48 Welbeck Street, London in 1799. He was also appointed Professor of Natural Philosophy at the Royal Institution, where he devoted his research to a variety of topics in both theoretical and applied science. He resigned in 1803 to devote more time to his medical practice, and the following year married Eliza Maxwell.

In 1809 Young was elected Fellow of the Royal College of Physicians and in 1811 was appointed physician to St George's Hospital, where he remained until his death. In 1814 he served on a committee to consider the dangers of the general introduction of gas into London, and in 1818 became Superintendent of HM Almanac Office.

Despite becoming seriously ill in early 1829, Young was determined to complete the rudiments of an Egyptian dictionary. He said it would be a satisfaction to see it finished, but that if he died beforehand, it would still be a great satisfaction never to have spent an idle day in his life.

Thomas Young died on 10 May 1829, aged 56. His monument in Westminster Abbey describes him as a 'man alike eminent in almost every department of human learning'.

THOMAS YOUNG: POLYMATH

Thomas Young's contributions to knowledge were wide ranging. He:
- Provided key insights into deciphering Egyptian hieroglyphs using the Rosetta Stone
- Devised a phonetic alphabet
- Established the wave theory of light
- Explained astigmatism and colour vision
- In *Young's modulus* gave an explanation of how different materials contract and expand
- Devised a technique for tuning musical instruments
- Coined the term Indo European after a comparative analysis of 400 languages
- Devised rule of thumb for determining a child's drug dosage
- Wrote several medical works, including *System of Practical Nosology* (1813) and *A Practical and Historical Treatise on Consumptive Diseases* (1815)

ROBERT MORRISON 1782–1834

Pioneer Protestant missionary in China

Robert Morrison, an Anglo-Scottish evangelist and missionary, was the first person to translate the whole Bible into Chinese and then publish it successfully.

Robert Morrison was born in Morpeth on 5 January 1782, the youngest son of a Scottish shoemaker and his English wife. Robert was not academically minded and fell into bad ways as a youth, but after a spiritual conversion he became a devout Christian and joined the Presbyterian church in 1798.

Morrison decided to become a missionary but promised his mother he would not take up his vocation while she was alive. After her death, in 1804, he was accepted by the London Missionary Society (LMS) and volunteered to go to China. Morrison then spent a year at a college for congregational ministers in Gosport. Back in London he spent two years studying Chinese, as well as attaining a basic knowledge of medicine from an introductory course for missionaries at Bart's.

Morrison's Chinese Bible: the start of the New Testament

Missionary in China

After his ordination, Morrison set sail for China and arrived in Canton on 7 September 1807, where he became proficient in both Mandarin and Cantonese. He also immersed himself in Chinese culture – he dressed in local costume, wore a false pigtail, let his fingernails grow long and ate Chinese food – but had to abandon the experiment due to ill health.

In 1809, living in Macao, Morrison married 17-year-old Mary Morton, with whom he had three children. Morrison began work on translating the scriptures while employed as a Chinese translator for the East India Company. This post, which he held until 1834, gave him a secure income and the right to remain in China.

Anglo-Chinese College in Malacca on the Malay Peninsula

Morrison was the first Protestant missionary to work in China and, although he made few converts, his translations provided the foundation for future missionary work. His task for the LMS was to make 'the translations of the Holy Scriptures, into the Chinese language the first and only object of his attention'. From 1815 to 1823 Morrison published three major works: a Dictionary of the Chinese Language, a Grammar of the Chinese Language and, most important, his translations of the Old and New Testaments. At this time he also set up a dispensary in Macao offering Western medical treatment to the Chinese.

Morrison's wife Mary died of cholera in 1821 and the following year he visited Singapore and Malacca, where he was instrumental in setting up the Anglo-Chinese College. In 1824 he returned to London, where he was made a Fellow of the Royal Society, presented his Chinese Bible to King George IV, set up the Language Institution for missionaries, and married Eliza Armstrong, with whom he had another five children.

The Morrison family returned to China in 1826. Relations between the Chinese and English grew increasingly strained and, in 1834, after the East India Company lost its China charter, Morrison lost his job. On 15 July 1835, Lord Napier made him Chinese Secretary and Interpreter with the rank of Vice Consul, but two weeks later, on 1 August, Robert Morrison died in his son's arms, aged 52.

ROBERT KNOX 1791–1862

Accomplice of body snatchers Burke and Hare

Robert Knox was a Scottish surgeon, anatomist and zoologist who studied at Bart's for a year after graduating from Edinburgh University. Before his involvement in the notorious Burke and Hare body-snatching case, Knox was the most popular lecturer in anatomy in Edinburgh.

Robert Knox was the eighth child of Robert and Mary Knox. His father was a schoolmaster at George Herriot's School in Edinburgh but young Robert attended the city's Royal High School.

In 1810 Knox enrolled as a medical student at Edinburgh University. He failed his first anatomy exam, but graduated in 1814 with flying colours under the instruction of John Barclay who ran an extra-mural school of anatomy.

Knox moved to London in 1815 to further his studies at Bart's. After a year he left for France, where he worked as a hospital assistant to the British Forces and administered to casualties resulting from the Battle of Waterloo. He returned to England with a party of the wounded.

In 1817 Knox went to South Africa for three years with the 72nd Highlanders. He returned to Britain in December 1820 and a few months later went to Paris for a year to study anatomy. On his return to Edinburgh, in 1822, Knox concentrated on the anatomy of the eye and also established a museum of comparative anatomy. He married his wife, Mary, in 1824 and took over John Barclay's School of anatomy in 1825.

Under suspicion

During 1828 Knox had more than 500 students but found that he was short of bodies to dissect. This led him to seek parliamentary sanction to acquire the unclaimed bodies of paupers. However, in the meantime, he was paying premium prices for cadavers regardless of their source. He even kept students on duty at night to receive the bodies, instructing his pupils to ask no questions and to pay the agreed price in cash.

In 1829 Knox came under suspicion for receiving a murder victim of the infamous body snatchers William Burke and William Hare. Some of Knox's professional colleagues, who felt he had too high an opinion of himself, took the opportunity to disassociate themselves. A private investigation, sponsored by a committee of Knox's friends, cleared him of any duplicity, but he remained under a cloud of suspicion and ceased to do any basic research on human anatomy.

In 1831 the Royal College of Surgeons in Edinburgh encouraged Knox's resignation as their museum conservator. His anatomy school was in decline and all his attempts to get a university post were in vain. Knox moved to London in 1842, where he gave lectures and worked as a journalist. Finally, in 1856, he was appointed pathological anatomist at the Free Cancer Hospital, taken on by William Marsden, the renowned Bart's trained surgeon, who courted controversy by employing him.

Later in life Knox said he had only three rules of health – temperance, early rising and frequent changes of linen. He died in the East End of London at the age of 71.

Satirical print of 1829 shows Robert Knox dissecting a cadaver. The 'dedication' reads 'to a most distinguished finishing lecturer – close of an obnoxious session'

THE LONDON BURKERS: BODY SNATCHERS WHO TURNED TO MURDER

In the early 19th century the legal supply of corpses for study was insufficient. The 1752 Murder Act permitted dissection only of the bodies of executed murderers. This produced about 55 bodies a year in London, when as many as 500 were required due to the opening of new medical schools in the city.

Body snatchers, called resurrectionists, had been stealing corpses for years. The crime was punishable only by a fine or imprisonment. For those involved, the trade paid well enough for them to run the risk of detection, particularly as the authorities often ignored what they considered to be a necessary evil.

To steal a body, the snatchers would often dig at the head end of a recent burial, break open the coffin, put a rope around the corpse and drag it out. A less obvious method was temporarily to remove an area of turf some distance away from a grave and then to dig a tunnel through which the grave robbers accessed the coffin and removed the body.

At St Sepulchre's Church in Giltspur Street, just across the road from Bart's, a parish watch-house was built to try to guard the graveyard. A notorious haunt of the racketeers was The Fortune of War pub, which was in easy reach of the graveyard and the hospital, where the corpses could be sold.

Burking

In 1830, a gang of London body snatchers – John Bishop, Thomas Williams, Martin Shields and James May, a former Smithfield butcher – changed its tactics from grave-robbing to murder. This gang – the London Burkers – modelled themselves on Burke and Hare. There was a premium for very fresh corpses and 'burking' (murder to acquire a cadaver) seemed a good way to get them.

One of the London Burkers' victims was a boy named Cunningham who had been found sleeping rough in the pig-market at Smithfield. The gang promised him lodgings, but instead drugged him with a mixture of warm beer, sugar, rum and laudanum and murdered him by attaching a cord to his feet and pitching him head first into a well. His body was undressed, placed in a bag and sold for eight guineas to a Mr Smith at Bart's.

Bishop and Williams confessed to this crime as well to others, in particular to the killing of another boy in what was known as the 'Italian Boy' murder. They were hanged in front of a crowd of thirty thousand at Newgate on 5 December 1831. Not surprisingly, they were 'anatomised' (made available for dissection). John Bishop, it is said, was found to be one of the best specimens ever dissected.

The Anatomy Act of 1832

The Burkers' dreadful activities led to the passing of the 1832 Anatomy Act. This gave free licence to doctors, teachers of anatomy and bona fide medical students to dissect donated bodies. It also gave them legal access to corpses that were unclaimed after death.

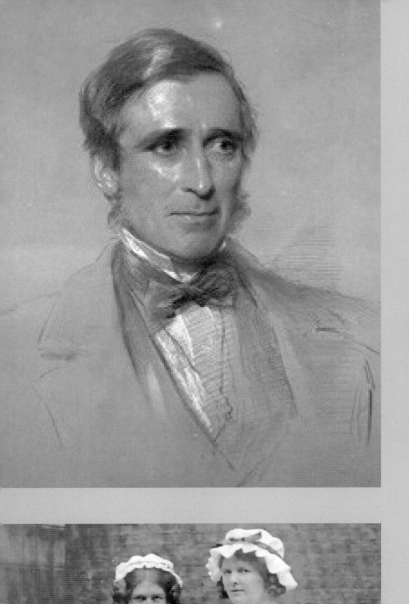

3

THE EARLY VICTORIANS

The Medical School at Bart's was now beginning to flourish and was the largest in London. In 1843 a residential college was built and James Paget became the first Warden. Within a few years, the number of students entering the Medical School each year was about 150 and the fees were 132 guineas (£138.60).

Meanwhile, William Lawrence, the surgeon, fell out with his colleagues; Richard Owen, the inventor of the term *Dinosauria*, disagreed with Charles Darwin, the evolutionist; and Charles West, the founder of Great Ormond Street Children's Hospital, had a reputation for being difficult.

There were mixed fortunes for others in this period. The kind William Marsden founded the Free Hospital and also the Marsden Cancer Hospital (both of which later received a royal charter). Frederick Skey was one of the first Fellows of the Royal College of Surgeons, but famously promoted the use of medicines over surgery. The empathetic prison doctor William Baly did sterling work before coming to a tragic end, while William Palmer was hanged for murder. Women continued to play an insignificant role at the hospital at this time and Frances Drake, the Matron, was obliged to resign.

WILLIAM LAWRENCE 1783–1867

Controversial surgeon who fell out with the medical profession and the church

William Lawrence had firm views on the meaning of life and suggested that the Bible might not be the last word on the nature of man. Also, his observations on inheritance made him a significant precursor of Darwin, whose 'On the Origin of Species' appeared 40 years after Lawrence's controversial lectures.

William Lawrence was born in July 1783, the elder son of a Cirencester doctor. His father was determined that William should become a surgeon and therefore packed him off to London at the age of 15 to be apprenticed for seven years at a premium of 400 guineas to the famous surgeon John Abernethy at St Bartholomew's Hospital.

Lawrence lodged with his boss and became his favourite pupil. He was so well regarded that in 1801 Abernethy appointed him his demonstrator of anatomy. Lawrence regularly attended meetings of the Medical and Philosophical Society of St Bartholomew's (founded by Abernethy in 1795 and to become the Abernethian Society) and it was there that he acquired the art of debate and repartee.

In 1805, aged 22, he received the diploma of the newly reconstituted Royal College of Surgeons. He was elected assistant surgeon at Bart's in 1813, the same year that he was elected a Fellow of the Royal Society. Soon after, he added various other appointments, including surgeon to the London Infirmary for Diseases of the Eye in 1814 and Professor of Anatomy and Surgery at the Royal College of Surgeons from 1815 to 1819.

Controversial lectures

Lawrence published his first set of lectures in 1816, causing a big fall out with Abernethy. Lawrence challenged Abernethy's explanation of John Hunter's theory of life. Both Hunter and Abernethy believed that life processes arose from a non-material, vital principle. Their view – known. as 'vitalism' – was that something was added from

> *It is strongly suspected that a Newton or Shakespeare excels other mortals only by a more ample development of the anterior cerebral lobes, by having an extra inch of brain in the right place.*
> **William Lawrence, 1819**

'outside' to give life to inanimate matter. Lawrence, on the other hand, believed that mental processes, including the thoughts of an individual, were purely a function of the brain, and 'that the motion proper to all living bodies, or in one word, life, has its origins in that of their parents'.

Abernethy and others at once attacked Lawrence for his 'materialism' and for undermining the moral welfare of the people. In 1819 Lawrence published a second book, *Natural History of Man*, which caused a storm for its supposed atheism. Supporters of Lawrence included Percy B. Shelley (who in 1811 had tried unsuccessfully to become a surgeon at Bart's) and his wife Mary. Shelley's poetry contains many references to the debate on vitalism, and Mary's novel *Frankenstein* supports Lawrence's dismissal of vitalism in favour of life as a result of physical organisation.

It is known that Charles Darwin owned a copy of Lawrence's book and was familiar with his views – and their reception. The furore that Lawrence faced for his attack on vitalism provided a foretaste of the controversy that would follow the publication of Darwin's *On the Origin of Species* in 1859.

The novel *Frankenstein* showed Mary Shelley's support for Lawrence

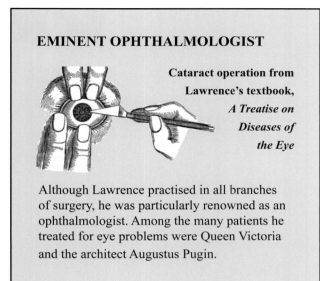

EMINENT OPHTHALMOLOGIST

Cataract operation from Lawrence's textbook, *A Treatise on Diseases of the Eye*

Although Lawrence practised in all branches of surgery, he was particularly renowned as an ophthalmologist. Among the many patients he treated for eye problems were Queen Victoria and the architect Augustus Pugin.

Moving on

Threatened with the loss of several of his positions, Lawrence withdrew his published lectures and looked to advance his career. He was appointed surgeon at Bart's in 1824 (a position he would hold until 1865) and eventually succeeded Abernethy as lecturer in surgery, but not before he had lectured for a time at the rival Aldersgate Medical School. In 1824, at a 'dinner for gentlemen educated at St Bartholomew's Hospital', Lawrence paid warm compliments to Abernethy. He congratulated him on the founding of the medical school at Bart's, which had removed the need for apprentices, and the two men were partially reconciled.

Lawrence, however, continued to ruffle feathers. He was a member of the radical group associated with *The Lancet*, launched in 1823 under the editorship of Thomas Wakley, which aimed to improve the medical profession and called for the remedying of 'abuses in the Royal College'.

Lawrence's career as a surgeon and lecturer was long and successful. Gradually he began to conform, joining the establishment he had previously outraged. In 1828, aged 45, he was elected onto the Council of the Royal College of Surgeons (by a single vote), which allowed him to push forward several much needed reforms. It is perhaps no coincidence that this was the year of his marriage to

Louisa Senior, the daughter of a socially ambitious Mayfair haberdasher. Lawrence's great-great grandson, Charles Gordon Clarke, considers that Lawrence's transformation from advanced thinker to silent observer of the next 50 years' progress was connected with his marriage and his wife's social ambitions.

In 1846, when delivering his second Hunterian Oration, Lawrence spoke contemptuously of ordinary medical practitioners. This caused a storm of dissent, to which Lawrence responded by folding his arms and saying, 'Mr President, when the geese have ceased their hissing I will resume'. He remained imperturbable, displayed his extraordinary talent as an orator, continued when he was ready – and was much applauded.

Lawrence's career prospered into old age. He served as President of the Royal College of Surgeons in 1846 and 1855, and was appointed Surgeon Extraordinary and then Serjeant-Surgeon to Queen Victoria. When he finally retired from Bart's he was given the complimentary title of 'Consulting Surgeon'. After having refused honours for many years, he accepted a baronetcy in the last months of his life – it is thought in the fruitless hope that it might help his son to marry an aristocrat.

William Lawrence died at his home on 5 July 1867, just before his 84th birthday. He had been attending the College in his official capacity and had suffered a stroke on the College stairs. His son, Sir Trevor Lawrence, became Treasurer of St Bartholomew's Hospital, and his grandson, Sir William Lawrence, was for many years a Bart's Almoner – one of four Governors who formed the hospital's Executive Committee.

William Lawrence, Bart's surgeon

WILLIAM MARSDEN 1796–1867

Saviour of the sick poor of London

A protégé of John Abernethy, William Marsden founded both the Royal Free Hospital and the Royal Marsden Hospital. He was known at the time as the compassionate surgeon.

William Marsden was born in Sheffield, the eldest of eight children. Aged 19, against his father's wishes and unbeknown to his parents, he left home for London to train as a surgeon. He travelled by stagecoach and, by chance, met and looked after a 12-year-old girl called Betsy Ann who had just lost her mother and was travelling alone. Four years later, when she was 16, they married and she was the love of his life until her death from cancer in 1846.

Soon after William's arrival in London he became apprenticed to Mr John Dale, a surgeon apothecary who

practised in the slums around Holborn. William looked after the drunk, depraved and diseased of the area who lived in dreadful squalour in housing that reeked of sewage. Gin shops abounded (with gin at 2d a nip). Consumption, venereal diseases and skin conditions were common, along with lice, fleas and vermin.

William Marsden began studying anatomy at Joshua Brooke's School but a new bye law passed in 1824 made it compulsory for medical students to attend lectures at certain hospitals, of which Bart's was one. He became a student of surgery under John Abernethy and qualified MRCS in 1827. Marsden was to follow Abernethy's methods throughout his life.

The founding of two hospitals

The year Marsden qualified he came upon a young girl on the steps of St Andrew's church on Holborn Hill. She was almost dead from disease and starvation. To his dismay, he was unable to get her admitted to Bart's as there was no time for him to obtain the letter of introduction signed by a governor that was needed for the admission.

Marsden was determined that something should be done, and less than six weeks later he set up a dispensary in Hatton Garden for the sick poor. They did not have to pay and they did not require a letter of introduction. Later, Marsden's dispensary was to become known as the Free Hospital. By 1832, its value was widely recognised as it was the only hospital that opened its doors to patients during the cholera epidemic. In 1837, it became the Royal Free Hospital after Queen Victoria became its patroness, and in 1843 it moved to Gray's Inn Road.

In 1851, five years after Betsy Ann's death, and despite considerable opposition to the idea of a specialist hospital, Marsden opened the Free Cancer Hospital in Westminster in 1851. He declared, 'I want to found a hospital for the treatment of cancer, and for the study of the disease, for at the present time we know absolutely nothing about it'. The hospital moved into a new, larger building in the Fulham Road, Chelsea in 1862. It received its royal charter in 1910 and became the Royal Marsden Hospital in 1954.

Marsden died of bronchitis on 16 January 1867. He had done much for others but his home life was not always rosy. Three of his four children died in childhood and his second marriage was unhappy.

The recently opened Royal Marsden Hospital in Chelsea's Fulham Road

GEORGE BODINGTON 1799–1882

Village doctor whose pioneering treatment of tuberculosis was ahead of its time

George Bodington's radical treatment of his patients who had tuberculosis was condemned by those in higher authority. He realised that consumptive patients would benefit from special hospitals and fresh air.

The deathbed of a tuberculosis sufferer. This was an all too common scene during George Bodington's lifetime

Although George Bodington was born in Buckinghamshire, he was descended from an old Warwickshire family of yeomen who had tilled their land since the reign of Henry VIII. At 16, after his schooling at Magdalen College School, Oxford, George left home to serve a surgical apprenticeship, first to a Mr Syner and then a year later to a Mr Wheelwright, a surgeon in the City. Subsequently he studied at Bart's and obtained the licence of the Society of Apothecaries when he was 26.

Little is known about Bodington during the next 15 years other than that he went on to practise in Erdington, near Birmingham, where he became involved in the care of many patients who had tuberculosis. He was an acute observer of his patients and noted that most important in the cure of consumption was fresh air and early morning walks – 'as much as the strength would allow'. He believed that English cold weather could never be too severe, and that the cooler the air his patients breathed in the better, and the more it promoted healing. To practise his method of treatment, Bodington took a property near his home in which he housed some of his patients. As well as making

sure they had plenty of fresh air, he gave them a nutritious diet and 'a proper quantity of wine', and made little use of drugs other than prescribing morphine as a sedative.

The 1840 essay

In an essay on the treatment and cure of pulmonary consumption, published in 1840, Bodington condemned the therapy currently advocated. He deplored the use of the two most commonly used drugs (digitalis and tartar emetic), treatment by means of bleeding, purgation and starvation, and also the shutting up of patients in rooms without fresh air. He suggested that there should be a certain class of practitioner who should specialise in the management of tuberculosis, and that hospitals should be established outside large towns because the common hospitals were the most unfit places for consumptive patients.

His essay was badly received by the medical hierarchy and it was later considered that Bodington had 'committed the cardinal sin of striking at orthodoxy'. The essay was violently attacked by *The Lancet* and Bodington became very disheartened. Due to the reception of his essay, he changed his interest from tuberculosis to mental disease and became proprietor of Drifford House Asylum in Sutton Coldfield, where he remained until his retirement in 1868.

Not the end of the story

When Bodington died in 1882, his obituary in *The Lancet* acknowledged that he had anticipated by many years the modern view in the treatment of tuberculosis and that it was remarkable that a village doctor should have reached these conclusions in 1840. Bodington had pioneered the sanatorium treatment of TB, which for many years was to become the main line of defence against the disease.

FREDERIC SKEY 1798–1872

Surgeon who strongly advised against using the knife

Frederic Skey worked at Bart's for many years but left for a time mid-career to become an important figure in the re-opening of the private Aldersgate School of Medicine, which was a serious rival to Bart's. He was an advocate for the use of tonics and stimulants in preference to bleeding, leeching, purgation and even surgery.

Frederic Skey was the second child of George Skey, a Russian merchant in London. After a private education, the young Frederic decided to become a doctor when he visited one of his father's cousins who was Inspector of Army Hospitals at Plymouth. While at Plymouth Frederic saw Napoleon Bonaparte being brought into the harbour on the ship *Bellerophon,* a sight which he never forgot and one which he often referred to for the rest of his life.

The defeated Napoleon being taken to Plymouth on board the *Bellerophon* in 1815 – an event witnessed by Skey

Apprenticeship

Having studied for a short time in Edinburgh and Paris, Skey became one of John Abernethy's last apprentices, for the privilege of which he, or more likely his father, paid 500 guineas. Skey was talented and highly valued by Abernethy and was entrusted with the care of some of the great man's patients. Due to Abernethy's influence Skey was appointed Demonstrator of Anatomy at Bart's in 1826 and Assistant Surgeon in 1827. However, his appointment met with considerable jealousy from William Lawrence and, after Abernethy's death, fresh arrangements were made. Skey resented the

reorganisation, which he considered unjust, and consequently resigned from Bart's in 1831.

The Aldersgate School of Medicine

Skey went on to lecture on surgery at the Aldersgate School of Medicine. The school, which was a private enterprise, had recently ceased functioning due to a dispute about the method of choosing new staff and Skey, along with several others, reopened the institution. It was a great success and soon became famous as a private teaching establishment and one of the largest medical schools in London. For many years it was a thorn in the flesh of neighbouring Bart's and seen to be the place where Bart's outsiders were 'plotting their comeback'.

Skey stayed at Aldersgate for more than 10 years, during which time his lectures were very popular and he formed many enduring friendships. His influence over the student body as a whole has been considered to have been possibly greater than that of any other contemporary teacher.

Back to Bart's

Skey returned to Bart's Medical School in 1843, following further fresh arrangements, to take the

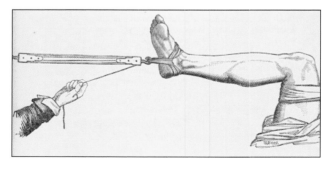

Treatment for a dislocated foot, an illustration from Skey's well received *Operative Surgery*, published in 1851

Illustration of head bandaging, from Skey's *Operative Surgery*

post of Lecturer in Anatomy. In this role, he was the first to suggest that students should undertake a preliminary examination in physics, chemistry and biology – but the issue was set aside. He was finally appointed Surgeon in 1854, staying in that post until 1864 when he reached the hospital's newly introduced retirement age of 65. He was then appointed Consulting Surgeon at Bart's, which allowed him to continue giving lectures there while also treating patients in his private practice.

Operative Surgery

Skey wrote a number of books, including *Operative Surgery,* published in 1851, in which he strongly advised against the use of the knife except as a last resort. This was good advice considering surgery was carried out without the benefit of anaesthesia. However, it was at about this time that he carried out plastic surgery on a girl who had fallen into a fire and been badly burned and horrifically scarred. The girl had gladly consented to Mr Skey's suggestion of an operation, which was to be watched by students. She was tied

Skey's treatment for a dislocated shoulder

to the operating table, as was customary, and the operation commenced. Within a few minutes, the girl's cries to be untied and to be allowed to keep her scarred body as it was, were the most frightful to be imagined. First one and then another student fainted, until all but the most determined few had left the theatre.

Commission on venereal disease

In 1864 Skey's friend, the Prime Minister Benjamin Disraeli, was responsible for his appointment as Chairman at the Admiralty of the first Parliamentary Commission to inquire into the best way of dealing with venereal diseases in the Navy and Army. This led to the passing of the Contagious Diseases Act (later repealed), which allowed police officers to arrest prostitutes in certain ports and army towns and to subject them to compulsory checks. If a woman was declared to be infected she was confined in what was known as a 'Lock Hospital' until 'cured'. The Act demonstrated the degree of double standards between men and women in Victorian society. Men

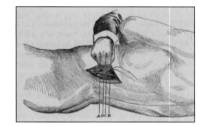

Procedure for tying the iliac artery, from *Operative Surgery*

were responsible for the demand for prostitutes, yet only women had to endure humiliating personal examinations and be effectively imprisoned.

Honours for Skey

Frederic Skey filled important positions and received many honours during his time at Bart's. He was one of the first 300 Fellows of the Royal College of Surgeons, was a President of the Royal Medico-Chirurgical Society, was elected a Fellow of the Royal Society and was appointed Companion of the Bath. Skey was considered to be a man of great intelligence, charm and energy, who showed exceptional diagnostic ability and considerable skill as a surgeon. He was also a good writer, clear lecturer and an excellent teacher.

RICHARD OWEN 1804–1892

Eminent scientist, driving force behind London's Natural History Museum and inventor of the term 'dinosauria'

Richard Owen was an exceptional comparative anatomist and palaeontologist, and through his efforts the natural history specimens in the British Museum were given a new home. However, he was arrogant and vindictive, dismissive of the work of others – including Charles Darwin –and became extremely unpopular.

Born in Lancaster in 1804, Richard Owen was the son of a merchant of the same name, who died when the lad was only five. Richard attended Lancaster Grammar School, where he was reputed to be both lazy and impudent, and was then briefly a midshipman in the Royal Navy.

Aged 16, in 1820, Owen returned to Lancaster and was apprenticed to a local surgeon, with whom he attended numerous fascinating post mortems at the local prison. He was so enthusiastic that on one occasion he bribed a prison guard to allow him to remove the head of a recently deceased black prisoner to enable him to make inter-racial comparisons – perhaps a foretaste of things to come.

In 1824, Owen was admitted to Edinburgh University but was not impressed by the quality of the teaching. He therefore enrolled at the private Barclay School of Anatomy to study comparative anatomy under John Barclay. A year later, with a recommendation from Barclay, Owen moved to London to become an apprentice at Bart's under John Abernethy. Owen became Abernethy's demonstrator, and in 1826 obtained his membership of the Royal College of Surgeons. From 1828 onwards, Owen gave regular lectures on anatomy at Bart's and in 1835 was officially appointed lecturer on comparative anatomy.

Iguanodon bones from Owen's History of British Fossil Reptiles

The Royal College of Surgeons

While at Bart's, with Abernethy's blessing, Owen also worked as an assistant to William Clift, the conservator at the Hunterian Museum at the Royal College of Surgeons. As assistant curator to the Hunterian Collection, Owen had the gargantuan task of identifying and cataloguing 13,000 of John Hunter's specimens. (This was necessary because Everard Home, Hunter's surgeon son-in-law, had burned most of Hunter's papers in order to publish the discoveries as his own.)

By 1830, Owen had labelled and identified every specimen and was so captivated by the project that he abandoned any idea of practising medicine. In 1835 he resigned from Bart's after being persuaded that holding dual posts would jeopardise his future. The following year he was appointed the first Hunterian Professor at the Royal College of Surgeons, a post he would hold for twenty years.

Owen became a popular lecturer, both to the general public and to royalty. He taught natural history to Queen Victoria's children and amazed the court with the fact that tadpoles grew into frogs. During his many years at the College, he came to be considered the foremost comparative anatomist in Europe and he enjoyed the privilege of receiving many interesting natural specimens, including exotic dead animals from London Zoo. Owen was elected Fellow of the Royal Society and during his lifetime published more than 600 scientific papers.

The Natural History Museum

In 1856, Richard Owen resigned from the Hunterian Museum to accept the newly created office of Superintendent of the Natural History Collections of the British Museum, situated in Bloomsbury. He immediately started a campaign to make the natural history department into a separate museum and won the support of William Gladstone MP, the future

Prime Minister. Owen succeeded in convincing the government of the benefits of his case and in 1864 a design competition was held for the new museum, which was to be built in South Kensington. The winner was Captain Francis Fowke but his sudden death led to the commision being

London's new Natural History Museum, opened in 1881

given to Alfred Waterhouse. Construction of the new building began in 1873 and the transfer of the natural history collections started in 1880. The museum opened to the public in 1881 and the move from Bloomsbury was completed in 1883.

Taxonomist

Over the years, Richard Owen acquired a remarkable knowledge of extinct animals and he named and described a vast number of living and fossil vertebrates. His most famous taxonomic act resulted from his examination of reptile-like bones found in southern England by Gideon Mantell. Owen concluded that the bones of *Iguanodon*, *Megalosaurus* and *Hylaeosaurus* represented a 'distinct tribe of Saurian reptiles', to which he gave the name *Dinosauria* (meaning 'terrible lizards') in 1842. To popularise the discovery, Owen helped in the creation of the first life-size (though anatomically inaccurate) sculptures of dinosaurs at Crystal Palace — and famously hosted an extravagant party in the belly of the Iguanodon.

Controversial figure

Owen became deeply involved in the public controversy regarding evolution. As a young man, he had firmly believed that each species had been uniquely designed and created by God. However, by the mid 1840s, his extensive study of comparative anatomy had led him to believe in a form of evolution. Although for a time it seems Owen was on good terms with Charles Darwin,

this changed after Darwin published *On the Origin of Species* in 1859. Owen rejected Darwin's theory of evolution by natural selection and wrote an anonymous article in the *Edinburgh Review* in which he criticised Darwin's reasoning and gave praise (in the third person) to his own work. Darwin knew immediately who had written the article and took umbrage.

Subsequently, Owen became a bitter spent force, being viewed as old-fashioned and very much at odds with the younger generation of naturalists. By all accounts Owen was not a pleasant man. He seldom admitted his own mistakes and did not always give credit where it was due. He was, however, an astute political activist and was one of the greatest scientific figures of Victorian England. Owen's most important gift to the nation was undoubtedly the founding of the Natural History Museum and in this he has left a lasting legacy to scientists and lay people alike.

Richard Owen married William Clift's daughter,

The Crystal Palace dinosaurs under construction in Sydenham

Caroline, and they had one son. Outliving them both he worked until he was 79. He accepted a knighthood in 1844, having previously declined the honour, and died ten years after his old rival Charles Darwin, on 18 December 1892.

GEORGE BUSK 1807–1886

Naval surgeon who gifted the Neanderthal 'Gibraltar skull' to the Royal College of Surgeons

George Busk helped establish a new branch of science – palaeoanthropology, the study of ancient humans from bones and footprints – and was an expert on cholera and scurvy.

The son of an English merchant, George Busk was born in Saint Petersburg, Russia. He came from an academic, high achieving family where much was expected, and young George was set to study medicine. After attending Dr Hartley's school in Bingley, Yorkshire he moved to London to serve a six-year apprenticeship under George Beaman at the Royal College of Surgeons, and completed his medical education at St Thomas's and Bart's.

Different types of Bryozoa

Seamen's Hospital

Busk's first job was as assistant surgeon with the Seamen's Hospital Society, which had been established in 1821 to care for sailors in the merchant navy and fishing fleets. After a short time on the *Grampus*, the society's first hospital ship, Busk transferred to its replacement, the *Dreadnought*, which was moored at Greenwich from 1831 to 1857. He was appointed full surgeon with the society and continued in this role at Greenwich for many years. While there he used the microscope to work out the pathology of cholera, made important observations on scurvy, and became a Fellow of the Royal Society.

A new career

After resigning his surgeon's post in 1855, Busk concentrated on biology and zoology. He was especially interested in the tiny moss animals called Bryozoa, on which he became a leading authority and a major contributor to many scientific societies in Britain. From 1856 to 1859 Busk was Hunterian Professor of Comparative Anatomy and Physiology at the Royal College of Surgeons and thus began

The *Dreadnought* in use as a hospital ship at Greenwich

his long association with the College. He was a Member of the Council from 1863 to 1880, Vice President (twice) and President in 1871.

George Busk was a proponent of evolution, and in 1864 – along with zoologist Thomas Huxley (known as 'Darwin's Bulldog') – he became a founder member of the X Club. This was a social dining club for scientists who wanted to engage in pure scientific research without the interference of religious dogma. Its members would be a powerful force in the politics of the Royal Society during the 1870s and 1880s.

In 1863 Busk attended a conference in Gibraltar during which he became particularly interested in palaeontology and its problems. He visited the Gibraltar Caves where he studied cave fauna and ethnology (the science that analyses and compares human cultures). One result of his visit was that he brought back the so-called 'Gibraltar skull', the first known adult Neanderthal skull, which he gave to the Royal College of Surgeons and is now at the Natural History Museum, London.

George Busk was married to his first cousin, Ellen Busk, and they had four daughters. He was very well respected and was 'a man of unaffected simplicity and gentleness of character, without a trace of vanity, a devoted friend and an upright, honest gentleman'.

THE EARLY DAYS OF THE ROYAL COLLEGE OF SURGEONS:
The Bart's connection

The London College of Surgeons had its origins in the 1540s, when the Company of Barbers and the Fellowship of Surgeons joined together to form the united Company of Barbers and Surgeons. By the 18th century, medicine had become an academic discipline and in 1745 the surgeons broke away from the barbers to form the Company of Surgeons. Percivall Pott and John Freke, both from Bart's, played a prominent role in the separation, and Pott became Master of Anatomy and subsequently Master of the Company in 1765.

Royal charter

In 1797 the surgeons moved from Surgeon's Hall in Old Bailey to a new a property in Lincoln's Inn Fields. A Bart's surgeon, William Long, had played an active role in the project, and became Master of the College during the first year at Lincoln's Inn. Then, in 1800, King George III granted the surgeons a royal charter, reputedly because Pott's son-in-law, James Earle, another Bart's surgeon, fostered the King's interest. Earle became Master in 1807. Another Bart's man, Charles Blicke, was Master in 1803 and 1810.

Further changes to the College charter were made in 1822, giving control to a President, two Vice Presidents and a Council. Abernethy became President amidst a bitter attack on the Council from his Bart's colleague William Lawrence, who argued that the College should recognise provincial hospitals for training purposes. Abernethy accepted Lawrence's view and by 1829 recognition had been given to schools of anatomy in several English towns.

There was also conflict over the proposed examination for the Fellowship. In the meantime, in 1846, 300 surgeons were nominated Fellows of the Royal College of Surgeons (FRCS) of London. These Fellows had the right to elect members of Council. Among the nominated Fellows were John Abernethy and John Bradley, both from Bart's – who immediately elected another Bart's man, Richard Welbeck, onto Council. The first fellowship examination was held in 1844 and one of the successful candidates was Bart's surgeon Luther Holden, who became President in 1879.

Dr or Mr?

The title 'Mr' for a surgeon originated in the 16th century, when surgeons were barber–surgeons and had no formal qualification, unlike physicians who all held a university degree. When the College of Surgeons received its royal charter, the Royal College of Physicians insisted that surgeons had to have a degree. Aspiring surgeons were therefore required first to study medicine, and those who were successful received the title Dr. However, after obtaining the diploma of Fellow of the Royal College of Surgeons the surgeons snubbed the physicians by reverting back to plain Mr, a practice that has remained to this day.

JOSEPH MEACOCK 1808–1880

Beadle at St Bartholomew's Hospital

Joseph Meacock, a hard-working cockney born about a quarter of a mile from the hospital, was a stalwart member of the Bart's workforce for 37 years.

Joseph Thomas Meacock (or Maycock) was born within the sound of Bow Bells, at Queen's Head Court in the parish of St Sepulchre, on 8 September 1808. He was the son of George Meacock, a carter who probably worked at Smithfield Market, and his wife Mary. Joseph started working at Bart's in 1829, when records show he was employed as a coal carrier and bathman. On 15 December 1831, aged 23, he married Mary Anne Middleditch, a tailor's daughter, at Christ Church Newgate Street. Between 1832 and 1850 they had six sons and two daughters.

Promotion to Beadle

Meacock was appointed in 1838 to the more reponsible job of a Beadle at Bart's. In 1844 he received further promotion, to Second Beadle, a post he would hold until his retirement in 1866. The 1841 census shows Joseph and his growing family living in Duke Street (now part of Little Britain) but in 1851 and 1861 they are included in the main hospital listings.

Resignation and retirement

Joseph Meacock resigned as a Beadle when he was 58 years old. His letter was read out at a House Committee Meeting in 1866, and stated that he had been laid up with effusion of the knee joint and general ill health, which 'I am sorry to say prevented me performing my duties regularly and causing extra work to devolve upon my fellow Servants I therefore under these circumstances feel compelled to place in your hands my resignation'. He concluded by saying, 'I earnestly hope you will take my past services into your kind consideration having had a large family to support since my appointment', and signed himself, 'Your most obedient humble Servant'.

Meacock's resignation was accepted and it was resolved unanimously that he should receive a pension of £70 per annum. In retirement, he is

known to have lived in Storks Road, Bermondsey. Mary, Joseph's wife of nearly 50 years, died early in 1880. A few months later, on 16 May, at the age of 71, Joseph Meacock died at Bart's, the hospital he had served so faithfully for so many years.

THE ROLE OF BEADLE

Historically, a major role of a Bart's Beadle had been to bring in sick people found lying in the streets of the City, but by Joseph Meacock's time a regular police force had been formed and the work of the four Beadles was centred round the hospital and its grounds.

The Beadles were attached to the Steward's Office and their tasks included sweeping the Square and entrance gates, carrying coal to the wards and delivering beer to the patients. They were not, however, allowed 'to keep company with any of the patients, nor to eat or drink with them in any victualling house'. When on duty at night, the Beadles were in charge of the gates to prevent patients from sleeping out, and they also had to clear the hospital from 'all idle and disorderly persons'.

Caricature of a Beadle, from *London Characters* by George Cruikshank

ERASMUS WILSON 1809–1884

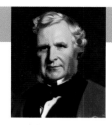

Eminent surgeon and dermatologist who paid for Cleopatra's Needle to be brought from Egypt

Erasmus Wilson achieved fame as a philanthropic dermatologist and champion of the poor. He was a strong advocate of sanitary reform, played an important part in the abolition of flogging in the Army, and pursued a keen interest in Egyptian antiquities.

Erasmus Wilson (full name William James Erasmus Wilson) was born in Marylebone on 25 November 1809. Aged 16, Erasmus became a pupil at the Cripplegate Dispensary in the City of London. He attended lectures at Bart's, given by Abernethy in his new lecture theatre, and those at the Aldersgate School of Medicine established by William Lawrence. Wilson became a licentiate of the Society of Apothecaries in 1830 and a member of the Royal College of Surgeons a year later. Subsequently he lectured at the Middlesex Hospital before becoming consulting surgeon to St Pancras Infirmary and assistant editor of *The Lancet* under Thomas Wakley.

Specialist in skin diseases

Wilson's interest in skin diseases arose from a wish to help the poor, and this specialisation gave him plenty of opportunity for philanthropy. He treated the skin problems of poor patients by prescribing – and often paying for – proper nourishment. By contrast, he treated the rich by advising them to give up luxuries and charged these patients 'accordingly'. It was said in social circles that as soon as he entered a room the company would start scratching!

Wilson firmly believed in the value of a daily bath and also helped bring Turkish baths to England. In his books he described the beneficial effects of spas, baths and thermotherapy on the skin. He praised the introduction of Public Baths and Wash-houses, and was an admirer of Edwin Chadwick, the champion of 19th-century sanitary reform.

The evidence given by Wilson in 1846 at an inquest (with Wakley as coroner) showed that a soldier had died from the after-effects of a flogging (a view opposed by the Army's own surgeons). Although the flogging of soldiers would not finally be abolished until 1881, Wilson is considered to have made an important contribution to this cause.

Wilson and the RCS

Wilson was elected a fellow of the Royal College of Surgeons in 1843. In 1868, he founded and financed a chair of dermatology, which he held from 1869 to 1877. Wise investments had made him a very rich man and he continued to support the College financially. He became Vice President in 1879–80 and President in 1881, the year he accepted a knighthood. In 1884 he was awarded the prestigious gold medal of the College.

In later years Wilson was beset by ill health and blindness. On his death in 1884, he left a vast fortune to his wife of over 40 years. The couple had no children and, after her death in 1886, the bulk of his estate, in excess of £200,000, went to the RCS.

CLEOPATRA'S NEEDLE

The obelisk now called Cleopatra's Needle had been gifted to Britain in 1817, but the British government had refused to pay for its transportation. Sixty years later, Erasmus Wilson agreed to pay the required £10,000 himself.

The obelisk left Alexandria encased in a metal shell, towed by the *Olga*, but became separated from the ship during a severe storm that cost six lives. Three months later the obelisk was found intact off Portugal. It was re-floated and towed to London, where it was erected in 1878 on its present site on the Embankment.

JAMES PAGET 1814–1899

Successful surgeon and pioneer of modern pathology who served St Bartholomew's Hospital for many years

From his youth James Paget was destined for greatness. He was clever and diligent and could have risen to the top as either a physician or a surgeon. He chose surgery but is now best remembered for describing the conditions that bear his name.

James Paget was the son of a successful brewer and ship owner in Great Yarmouth. He was born on 11 January 1814, the eighth of 17 children (of whom nine survived). Unfortunately his father's business ceased to prosper and he could not afford to send James to Charterhouse as had been possible for his three oldest sons, so as a result, when James was 13, he was sent to a local, small private school.

Apprenticeship and Bart's student

In 1830, aged 16, James made the decision to be a surgeon and became apprenticed for 100 guineas to Charles Costerton in Great Yarmouth, where he gained much practical experience. In his spare time, with his brother Charles, he studied and wrote

Trichina spiralis **cysts**

a book on the flora and fauna of Great Yarmouth. James's meticulous attention to detail and his ability to catalogue were evident and later he wrote 'the knowledge was useless; the discipline of acquiring it was beyond price'.

In 1834 James Paget enrolled as a student at Bart's, where his older brother George, a physician, paid his fees. James won all four prizes – medicine, surgery, chemistry and botany – in 1835 and 1836. He was, however, unable to afford the fee demanded by surgeons for the office of dresser, and instead acted as clinical clerk under the physician Peter Mere Latham.

The teaching at Bart's was of variable quality and the students were expected to work with little guidance. Paget therefore spent much time studying and carrying out dissections on his own. One day, in 1835, while carrying out a dissection with the aid

Paget's eloquent lectures attracted many students to Bart's

of a microscope borrowed from the Natural History Museum, Paget noticed some white specks in the muscle of the cadaver. Richard Owen confirmed Paget's finding that the specks were cysts containing worms. The parasite became known as *Trichina spiralis* (also *Trichinella spiralis*) and was found to be acquired through eating unhealthy pork.

Early career and promotion

James Paget became a Member of the Royal College of Surgeons in 1836 but it took seven years of poorly paid work before he achieved a satisfactory position at Bart's. In the meantime, Paget supported himself by teaching and writing. He was sub-editor of the *Medical Gazette* and wrote for the *Quarterly Review*, contributing articles on various topics including cancer, syphilis and typhoid as well as surgical conditions. In addition he was appointed curator at the Bart's Museum, and in 1839 was made demonstrator of morbid anatomy.

At last, in 1843, Paget gained a promotion and became lecturer on general anatomy and physiology.

From 1843 until 1851 he was also Warden of Bart's first hall of residence for students – where he was disturbed by the young men's dissipation and lack of decorum. At the same time he continued compiling catalogues for the Bart's and Hunterian Museums.

Later career and honours

In 1846 James Paget was nominated one of the original fellows of the Royal College of Surgeons of England, and the next year he became Aris and Gale Professor of Anatomy at the College. Also in 1847, Paget was made an assistant surgeon at Bart's, although there was some opposition to his appointment on the grounds that he had not been a dresser or house surgeon at the hospital, which had until then been considered necessary qualifications.

Paget was elected a fellow of the Royal Society in 1851 and that same year also set up in private practice near Cavendish Square as a consultant. He was extremely successful and his surgical practice was soon the largest in London.

MARRIED LIFE

After an eight-year engagement, James Paget married Lydia North, a clergyman's daughter, in 1844. He commented that his was 'a marriage blest with constancy of perfect mutual love and not once disturbed'. Lydia was a gentle, compassionate and devoted wife.

As a new bride, Lydia Paget lived in the Warden's house in Little Britain. This was in earshot of the operating theatre, and she suffered greatly on hearing the cries of the patients. Her relief was great when two years later anaesthesia was first used during an amputation in the hospital. Lydia was heard to say that she was surprised that a day for national thanksgiving had not been set aside to commemorate the discovery of anaesthetics. This momentous breakthrough was undoubtedly the most important surgical development during James Paget's lifetime.

The Pagets had four sons and two daughters, all of whom survived them. Lydia Paget died in 1895, a loss from which James never recovered.

EPONYMS FOR JAMES PAGET

Paget's abscess; Paget's cells; Paget's disease of bone; Paget's disease of the nipple; Paget's extramammary disease; Paget's sign; Paget-von Schrötter disease

---

In 1861 Paget finally became full surgeon at Bart's and continued in this role until 1871, when he resigned, aged 57, due to a period of ill health resulting from blood poisoning acquired while performing a post mortem. However, he did not leave Bart's completely as he was appointed consulting surgeon at the hospital.

Paget had become Surgeon-Extraordinary to Queen Victoria in 1858, while still not a full surgeon at the hospital. From 1867 he held the office of Serjeant-Surgeon Extraordinary to the Queen, and then in 1877 became her Serjeant-Surgeon. Paget was created a baronet in 1871, the year he successfully treated the Prince of Wales for typhoid. It was said by Richard Owen that Paget had 'had the choice to be the first physiologist in Europe or to have the first surgical practice in London with a baronetcy' – he chose the latter.

James Paget was Vice-President of the Royal College of Surgeons in 1873 and 74, and President in 1875. He also held the presidency of other medical societies and from 1883 until 1895 was Vice-Chancellor of the University of London.

This charming and kindly man died on 30 December 1899. His funeral in Westminster Abbey was presided over by his son Francis, Bishop of Oxford. James Paget had lived his life according to his family motto: *'Labor ipse voluptas'* – 'Work is itself a pleasure'.

Rudimentary anaesthesia equipment as used by Paget

WILLIAM BALY 1814–1861

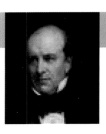

From Prison to the Palace – a physician who was a friend to people from every rank in life

As prison doctor at London's Millbank Penitentiary, William Baly established himself as a specialist in the hygiene of prisons. He was also a successful physician at Bart's. Baly's life was cut short when he was tragically killed in an accident at the age of 46.

William Baly was born in Kings Lynn, Norfolk in 1814. On leaving the local grammar school in 1828 he was apprenticed to a Dr Dingle in Emsworth. Two years later he arrived at Bart's to continue his studies and in 1834 obtained the diplomas of the Royal College of Surgeons and the Society of Apothecaries. He then studied in Paris and Heidelberg before gaining his MD in Berlin in 1836.

The Millbank Penitentiary seen across the Thames

Millbank Penitentiary

In 1840 the government appointed Baly to report on the state of the Millbank Penitentiary, and in 1841 he was made physician of the prison. Following the opening of a new 'model prison' at Pentonville in 1842, the status of Millbank was downgraded and it became the holding depot for convicts sentenced to deportation. The convicts were held there in solitary confinement for three months while awaiting a decision on their deportation destination.

Many of the Millbank inmates suffered from diseases such as dysentery, cholera, tuberculosis and scurvy. By adding a quantity of lightly cooked potatoes to the prisoners' diet, Baly succeeded in completely eliminating cases of scurvy at the prison. Baly's work at Millbank provided material for his Goulstonian Lectures on Dysentery, given in

1847. It also gave him prominence as a government adviser. His study *On the mortality in prisons, and the diseases most frequently fatal to prisoners* showed that prisoners were twice as liable to die as other men of the same age. In 1854, with William Withey Gull from Guy's Hospital, Baly wrote a two-part report on the 1854 cholera epidemic.

Other appointments

While at Millbank, Baly held various positions at Bart's. In 1841 he was made lecturer in forensic medicine, despite some opposition as he was not an Oxbridge man. In 1854 he was elected assistant physician, but gave this up a year later to become joint lecturer on medicine with George Burrows. Baly was elected Fellow of the Royal College of Physicians and a Fellow of the Royal Society, and was considered to be 'one of the brightest ornaments of the medical profession'. In 1859 he was appointed Physician Extraordinary to Queen Victoria, joined the General Medical Council as Crown Representative, and was nominated Censor for the Royal College.

Tragedy

Baly prize medal awarded by the Royal College of Physicians

Baly's life and career came to an abrupt end on 28 January 1861 when he took a train from Waterloo to Guildford. The train was derailed near Wimbledon and although 19 passengers were injured, the only one killed was William Baly who was crushed to death. His premature death, at the age of 46, occurred before he had attained the rank of full physician at Bart's. The hospital lost of one of its most brilliant servants, and society was deprived of a man devoted to the public good.

CHARLES WEST 1816–1898

Founder of Great Ormond Street Hospital for Children who warned against treating children as miniature adults

Charles West was an expert in the field of childcare and established the first children's hospital in the United Kingdom. He was a physician at Bart's and had a reputation for being difficult.

The son of a Baptist minister, Charles West was born in London on 8 August 1816. Aged 15, in 1831, he was apprenticed to a Buckinghamshire general practitioner, and was then a student at Bart's from 1833 to 1835. As a Nonconformist he was barred from Oxbridge, and therefore continued his studies in Europe, graduating as Doctor of Medicine in Berlin in 1837. After his return he started an unsuccessful private practice in London before moving to Ireland to study midwifery.

West was made a member of the Royal College of Physicians in 1842 and became Chief Physician  at the Waterloo Road Dispensary for Sick and Indigent Children in London. At this time the streets of London were littered with malnourished waifs and strays, and the mortality rate among poor children was appalling. The Dispensary provided a valuable 'outpatient' service but West's wish for it to be a children's hospital was not met.

While at the Dispensary, West returned to Bart's to teach midwifery. He also lectured on children's diseases at the Middlesex Hospital. His *Diseases of Infancy and Childhood*, published in 1841, was the first proper English textbook on paediatrics.

Great Ormond Street Hospital

West's mission to found a children's hospital persisted, and in 1850 he joined with Henry Bence-Jones and others, including Lord Shaftesbury, to pursue this end. The Hospital for Sick Children opened its doors in Great Ormond Street on 14 February 1852, and West became Chief Physician. At first, there were only two ten-bed wards – insufficient to cope with the dreadful diseases and childhood suffering. The beds were in much

The new Great Ormond Street Hospital, opened in 1875

demand, especially during the cholera epidemic, and families who could afford a doctor were sent away. Many people, including Charles Dickens (a friend of West's), raised money for the hospital. In 1858 the next-door property was purchased, increasing the bed tally to 75. Then, between 1871 and 1875, a new, larger, purpose-built hospital was built in what had been the gardens of the original houses.

Another of Charles West's ambitions was to train paediatric nurses. He was aware that children should be nursed differently from adults and therefore wrote his *How to Nurse Sick Children*, published in 1854, five years before Nightingale's *Notes on Nursing*.

Friction

West continued to work at Bart's, where he was in charge of 13 beds, gave lectures on midwifery and wrote his *Diseases of Women*, published in 1856. He resigned in 1861, seemingly because the hospital did not recognise the importance of his role.

He remained at Great Ormond Street until 1877, when he resigned after a series of highly publicised disagreements with the Management Committee. Sadly, his role in the development of children's healthcare went largely unrecognised in his lifetime, perhaps because of his feuding with both hospitals and his unpopularity with other physicians.

Charles West married twice and had a son and a daughter. He died in Paris in 1898 at the age of 82.

Surgeon who loved to study and teach anatomy

Luther Holden was one of the last members of the school of surgeons who based their surgery on anatomy. He cared little for private practice but championed his pupils.

Born on 19 December 1815, in his grandfather's house in Birmingham, Luther Holden was the second son of the Rev. Henry Holden and his wife and cousin Mary. He had four brothers, two of whom went into the church, and three sisters. He was educated by his father, who ran a small private school, and then spent a year in Le Havre where he learnt to speak fluent French.

At 17, Luther Holden was apprenticed to Edward Stanley, a surgeon at Bart's, and lived with him and his family for five years at Lincoln's Inn Fields. During this time Stanley came to admire Holden both for his skills as a dissector and for his desire to teach. Holden continued his studies by spending a year in Berlin and a year in Paris, where anatomy was far better taught than it was in England.

On his return to London, in 1838, Holden became a Member of the Royal College of Surgeons, and to make ends meet began teaching anatomy to private pupils, one of whom was William Palmer, the so-called Rugeley Poisoner. Holden was appointed Surgeon to the Metropolitan Dispensary in 1844, and the same year, along with 24 others, received the newly established diploma of the Royal College of Surgeons after passing the first examinations for Fellowship of the College.

Anatomy and writings

In 1846 Holden was appointed Demonstrator of Anatomy at Bart's, a position he would hold for 15 enjoyable and fruitful years. Then, in 1859, he was elected Lecturer on Descriptive and Surgical

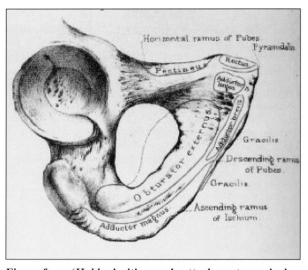

Figure from *'Holden'* with muscle attachments marked

Anatomy, jointly with Frederick Skey.

Holden's painstaking work in the dissecting room resulted in three highly regarded educational works. His *Manual of the Dissection of the Human Body* was first published in 1851 and was then later republished in enlarged form, edited by John Langton and with Holden's name in the title.

The greatest of Holden's books was *Human Osteology*, published in 1855, which marked a distinct advance in the study of the human skeleton. It was remarkable for its fine illustrations, drawn by Holden himself, which demonstrated his new system for marking the attachment of the muscles. (Henry Grey quickly adopted this system for use in his famous *Anatomy*, and gave full credit to Holden.) Although Holden's osteology was considered too simple in style for some, many admitted that it taught as much as the average student could hold in their memory. A much later surgeon, Lawson Tait, declared that if a student knew his *Holden* then that was quite enough.

In his third major work, *Landmarks, Medical and Surgical*, first published as a treatise in 1866 and then as a book in 1876, Holden showed how much anatomy can be learnt from studying the surface of the body without the skin being broken.

Holden the surgeon

Holden was kept waiting many years before his wish to join the surgical staff at Bart's was granted. At last, in 1860, he was elected assistant surgeon at the age of 45. He then rose up the ranks faster than he might have expected – due to the introduction of a new compulsory retirement age – and became full surgeon five years later.

Holden was one of the last members of the school of surgeons who based their practice on anatomy and he is not particularly remembered for his surgical attainments. He carried out herniotomies and other minor surgical procedures with skill, and he was a good, clinical general surgeon because of his knowledge of anatomy and physiology and how they applied to surgery.

It has been suggested that if Holden had been appointed surgeon sooner, he might have matched the skills of great surgeons like James Paget, but this seems unlikely. Holden did not have antiseptics or aseptic methods at his disposal, and although he was physically brave, he apparently lacked mental courage. It was said that he preferred clearing a five-barred gate on the hunting field to performing a major operation.

His ingenuity was evident in his invention of a gadget, known as 'Holden's sausage', to provide continuous digital pressure to treat popliteal aneurysms arising from the poor treatment of syphilis. However, it depended on the services of a continuous relay of students, was painful for the patient, was rarely successful and, not surprisingly, soon fell into disuse.

Holden the teacher

It was no secret that Luther Holden's first love was the teaching and coaching of his pupils, who, in return, enjoyed his friendship and support. Apparently his patience was second to none and he succeeded in teaching even those who were less able and who had been given up on by

Sensitive portrait of the handsome Luther Holden, painted by John Everett Millais

everyone else. He was a highly popular examiner with the medical students, but was considered by some of his colleagues to be too lenient. He felt he knew how to distinguish nervousness from ignorance, and he was certainly able to gain the confidence of even the shyest of young men.

Holden was a Member of Council at the Royal College of Surgeons, served for many years on various examination boards, was Vice President in 1877 and 1878, President in 1879 and Hunterian Orator in 1881.

Personal matters

Luther Holden married twice but had no children. His first wife, Frances Sterry, eight years his senior, was 43 years old when they married in 1851. Following her death, he remarried in 1868. His second wife, another Frances Sterry, was the daughter of his first wife's brother. She was 27 when they married and he was 52. Both wives had independent fortunes, and his second wife was well known for her philanthropy.

Holden resigned his hospital appointments in 1880 at the age of 65 and was made Consulting Surgeon. He then spent much time travelling the world, visiting places as far flung as Australia, India and Japan. With his wife, he moved from London to Pinecroft, near Ipswich, where he loved the country life and continued to be a very handsome figure on his horse.

Luther Holden lived to a ripe old age, dying when he was in his 90th year, on 6 February 1905. Generous and kind, he made a handsome bequest to St Bartholomew's Hospital and also bequeathed £3,000 to endow a scholarship in surgery in the Medical School.

FRANCES DRAKE 1816–1892

Matron at St Bartholomew's Hospital who believed nurses were no more than servants

Frances Drake was in post soon after the introduction in 1860 of Florence Nightingale's nursing training reforms. Bart's, however, continued without a nursing school for another 16 years.

Born in Clifton, Gloucestershire on 31 May 1816, Frances was the second of James and Emily Elton's five children. By 1820 she was living with her well-to-do parents in Tiverton, Devon. In 1842 she married Alfred Drake, a solicitor, in Oakhampton and the young couple went to live on the Quay in Barnstaple. After 10 years of marriage, Alfred died. There were no children but Frances was left with insufficient money to live without working. Having always lived in a home with servants, Frances took a job as housekeeper to a widowed cloth merchant and his adult sons in Ashton upon Mersey.

After moving to London, and gaining some hospital experience at the Foundling Hospital, Mrs Drake was appointed Matron at Bart's in 1865. She was clearly not a trained nurse and it would appear from the outset that she considered the nurses at the hospital to be little better than charwomen.

Although Mrs Drake was aware of Nightingale's work and 'sympathised with the new movement', she was not proactive in her own hospital. She did, however, employ 'scrubbers', who worked from 7 a.m. to 11 a.m., to relieve the nurses of the task of cleaning the floors and staircases. This persuaded the governors that a better type of woman might now be keen to nurse. However, this was a forlorn hope, as the nurses were still expected to clean grates and furniture, cook the sisters' meals, light the fires, wash the patients' dishes and sweep the wards early in the morning. Nurses' conditions did begin to improve after their sleeping accommodation was enlarged and their rotation of duty changed, but no training was offered.

The Nursing School proposal

As early as 1861, Nightingale had communicated with James Paget to encourage the introduction of a nursing school at Bart's. However, nothing was done until Sir Sydney Waterlow became Treasurer of the hospital in 1874. He at once resolved to establish a school to supply Bart's with its own trained nurses. Mrs Drake was already 60 and was not enthusiastic. However, in April 1876 the governors approved the scheme and allocated £100 for the first year expenses. The pupils, known as probationers, would attend for a year during which they would be given 'regular instruction in the technical knowledge of nursing' and would receive a salary of £10. One probationer would be attached to each ward but could be reallocated at Matron's discretion. At the end of the year, satisfactory students would receive a certificate of competency. The first Bart's Nurses' Home, converted from three houses in Little Britain, was opened in 1877. It included the hospital's first dining room, where breakfast and dinner were provided daily.

Bart's nurses of 1908 dressed up in uniforms from earlier times

Frances Drake was not in tune with the changes. She loathed the idea that nursing might be a suitable career for ladies, and tried to dissuade applicants to the school whose background was not working class. In 1878 the governors asked her to resign to make room for a Matron who was a qualified nurse. With a pension from Bart's, Frances Drake spent her retirement in London and Tiverton. She died in London on 16 January 1892.

THE ACCOUNT OF A NURSE PROBATIONER AT BART'S IN 1877
A longer version of this account, by a future 'Sister Casualty', appeared in the League of St Bartholomew's Hospital Journal of 1902.

I came in on May 1st 1877, one of a batch of 12 probationers, the first to be trained at St Bartholomew's Hospital. The Matron, Mrs Drake, greatly disapproved of such innovations as 'lady-nurses' and tried hard to dissuade me from entering when I came up to be interviewed.

We all arrived one morning and put on our uniform [dark grey cotton dresses and small caps of a standard pattern]. This was quite different from the so-called 'staff nurses' who wore brown merino dresses, aprons without bibs, and caps or no caps as they liked.

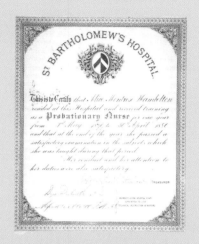

Certificate awarded for completing a year as a probationer

I shared a room opening on to the ward with the staff nurse who was drunk and I did not get much rest. Drunkenness was very common among staff nurses who were chiefly women of the 'char-woman' type, frequently of bad character with little or no education, and few of them with even an elementary knowledge of nursing.

Among the sisters, there was already some improvement. Some there were still of whose virtues the less said the better, and some were wholly untrained – a knowledge of nursing not being in those days a necessary qualification for that special work. A few had been trained at the 'Nightingale' home; they had considerable experience and were, moreover, clever and capable women of superior character. The sisters wore blue merino dresses without either caps or aprons.

Sir Dyce Duckworth or Mr Willett lectured us or gave us a practical demonstration once a week. Sir Dyce would take us into the wards and give us a lesson on bed-making, poultice making or show us how to get the patients in and out of the bath. We were known as 'Ducky's lambs'.

We picked up what we could. Everyone took a great interest in us. Dr Griffiths taught me to take temperatures. We were on duty from 7 a.m. until 10 p.m. Twice a week we were supposed to go off duty for 2 hours, 6–8 p.m., and to have half a day (3 p.m.–9 p.m.) once a fortnight.

Patients were not nursed then, they were 'attended to'. They had their beds made once a day, the bad cases had their sheets drawn at night. You thought nothing of having 14 or 15 poultices to change. All wounds, of course, suppurated, and required dressing or poulticing twice or three times a day.

At the end of the year we passed an examination but I believe marks were not awarded until Miss Manson [later Mrs Bedford Fenwick] came. We were awarded certificates and offered posts as staff nurses, which few were bold enough to accept on account of the existing conditions of things.

I have really no words in which to describe the state the hospital was in when I came as a probationer, and if I had you would say the account was not fit for publication. It was many years before the nursing staff were treated with anything approaching respect.

JOHN LEECH 1817–1864

Caricaturist and cartoonist who helped make Punch magazine a success

John Leech began medical training at Bart's but had to leave due to changed family fortunes. His artistic talents meant that he had no difficulty making a good living as an illustrator and political satirist.

John Leech catches Mr Punch at work in the office

The son of the proprietor of the London Coffee House on Ludgate Hill, John Leech was born into comfortable circumstances. His father (also called John) was a respected and cultured man who passed on his skill with a pencil to his son. At a very early age, the young John was already showing an exceptional talent for drawing.

In 1833, aged 16, Leech left Charterhouse School and began to study medicine at Bart's, where his anatomical drawings immediately won him much praise for their accuracy and beauty. Leech's

A painting of the then popular game of croquet

medical career, however, was to be shortlived – the bankruptcy of his father gave him little alternative but to end his medical studies and turn instead to illustration to support himself. His first published work, *Etchings and Sketchings,* a short collection of comic character studies from the London streets, appeared under the name of A. Pen, Esq., in 1835.

Satirical works

Over the next few years Leech made humorous drawings for pamphlets, including *Portraits of the Children of Mobility*, and also supplied illustrations to literary magazines, notably *Bentley's Miscellany*

Rape of the Sabine women - from *Comic History of Rome*

(edited by Charles Dickens) and *The London Magazine*. Perhaps because he had spent some time in France, Leech brought a new approach to social satire in England. A critic described his work as 'less grotesque, less boisterous, less exaggerated, nearer to the truth and to ordinary experience' than that of either James Gillray or George Cruikshank.

The satirical magazine, *Punch,* was founded in 1841, and Leech immediately became one

Beautifully executed watercolour of a hunting scene

of its leading artists. Over the next 23 years, he contributed 3,000 illustrations and some 600 political cartoons and scenes of everyday life. His weekly sketches for *Punch* show the change in popular taste 'from the savagery of the Regency caricature to the gentler world of bourgeois domestic humour.' Leech's *Substance and Shadow*, published in *Punch* in 1843, criticised artists

Substance and Shadow – the first satirical cartoon

for ignoring social issues such as poverty, and is noteworthy for being the first satirical drawing to be referred to as a cartoon.

Popular illustrations

In addition to his satirical work, Leech also made numerous illustrations for novels, ballads, short stories and children's books, most notably

Frontispiece to Dickens's *A Christmas Carol*

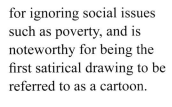

providing illustrations for *A Christmas Carol* written by his friend Charles Dickens. Many of Leech's most popular illustrations, mainly from the 1850s, were of sporting subjects, in particular hunting.

Some of the best of these appeared in the *Illustrated London News* from 1859 to 1863.

Leech's prolific body of work shows his skill at using different techniques: drawing, etching, painting with watercolours, lithography and wood engraving. In 1862 he held a very successful exhibition of some of his *Punch* drawings that had been enlarged by a mechanical process and then coloured in by the artist himself.

The adults pass comments as the children engage in boxing

Leech was an indefatigable worker – perhaps driven by the need to earn more and more money so that he and his wife, Anne, and their two children could move to larger and larger houses – which taxed his strength. This tall, handsome, likeable man suffered from angina and died at the young age of 47 from a heart attack. When the sculptor John Flaxman first saw John Leech drawing at the age of three, Flaxman said 'he will astonish the world' – and this proved to be the case.

Leech's humorous hunting scenes were especially popular

'The Rugeley Poisoner' –
a serial killer or an innocent man?

William Palmer was found guilty of murder in one of the most notorious cases of the 19th century. He was convicted at the Old Bailey and was executed in front of thousands at Stafford Gaol.

The trial of William Palmer at the Old Bailey in London in May 1856

The career of William Palmer of Rugeley, Staffordshire got off to a bad start. He was apprenticed first to a Liverpool chemist, but was dismissed after only three months for seducing a girl and robbing his masters. A second apprenticeship, with a local surgeon, ended when he was discovered to be both a swindler and a seducer. He then entered the Stafford Infirmary as a walking pupil but again was sacked – for becoming very involved with the dispensing of medicines, which was forbidden.

Intent on becoming a doctor, Palmer went to London in 1846 to train at Bart's. There he ate and drank of the best, spent days and nights in riotous living, gambled heavily and apparently fathered at least 14 illegitimate children. Although he collected his diploma, he was described by James Paget as 'idle, dissolute, extravagant, vulgar and stupid'.

Suspected poisonings

William Palmer, surgeon, returned to Rugeley and married his wife, Ann, in 1847. A number of suspicious deaths ensued. The couple's first child survived but their next four children all died from violent convulsions in infancy. Another possible victim was his mother-in-law who, before moving in with the family, reputedly commented, 'I know I shall not live a fortnight' – and she was right! Other suspected poisonings were of a man who had lent him £600, and of Palmer's illegitimate daughter. Next was his wife, who died of cholera, but on whom Palmer had taken out life insurance. Still heavily in debt, Palmer attempted to take out a life policy on his brother, Walter, who was a drunkard. On Walter's death the insurance company became suspicious and refused to pay up.

The death of John Cook

On 14 November 1885, Palmer lost heavily on a horse in the Shrewsbury Handicap Stakes. His friend John Cook won £3,000 and they went to celebrate together. Cook was violently sick after drinking brandy, which he complained had burnt his throat, and he allegedly told two friends that, 'I believe that damn Palmer has been dosing me'. Three days later, having apparently recovered, Cook again met up with Palmer and was again sick. Palmer then gave Cook some soup, which might have been doctored as a chambermaid who took two sips fell ill and Cook's vomiting worsened.

On 18 November Palmer collected debts on behalf of Cook, purchased two grains of strychnine and gave pills to Cook. Palmer purchased six more grains of strychnine on 21 November and gave pills to Cook three times over a period of several hours. Cook's limbs became rigid and he died in agony. Cook's stepfather, William Stevens, on behalf of the family visited Palmer on 23 November and

Dr Alfred Taylor (left) and a colleague performing the Marsh test on samples taken from the body of John Cook

was told that Cook's betting books had been lost. Stevens successfully requested an inquest into Cook's death, while Palmer obtained a death certificate from an 80-year-old Dr Bamford, who listed the cause of death as 'apoplexy'.

Post mortem and inquest

A post mortem of Cook's body was held on 26 November, watched by Palmer who interfered with the procedure. The contents of the stomach were spilt when Palmer bumped into one of the physicians. Then Palmer took a jar containing the stomach away for 'safe keeping'. On its return, the stomach was found to have two slits in it. Complaining that the specimens were too poor to be of use, Dr Alfred Taylor ordered a second post mortem, which took place on 29 November. Palmer now contacted his friend Samuel Cheshire, the post master, and persuaded him to intercept any letters addressed to the coroner or solicitor. Cheshire was able to inform Palmer that no poison had been found in Cook's body. Palmer immediately sent the coroner some 'nice pheasants and a good hare', a £10 note and a letter stating that he had seen in 'black and white' that no poison had been found and that the coroner should give a verdict of 'died of natural causes and thus end it'. Although Dr Taylor had found no evidence of strychnine, he was convinced that Cook had

been poisoned and argued at the inquest that the description of Cook's death indicated tetanus and that the tetanus had been produced by strychnine. The verdict was that the 'Deceased died of poison wilfully administered to him by William Palmer'.

Arrest, trial and execution

Palmer was arrested and held at Stafford Gaol. The bodies of Ann Palmer and Walter Palmer were exhumed. Walter's was too badly decomposed but Anne's contained antimony and inquest verdicts of wilful murder were returned in both cases.

The Central Criminal Court Act was subsequently passed to allow the trial to be held at the Old Bailey as it was felt that a fair trial could not be held in Staffordshire as there was so much local prejudice following lurid newspaper reports. William Palmer's trial took place in London in May 1856 and lasted 12 days. In the event he was tried only for the murder of Cook, for which he was found guilty. He was convicted on circumstantial evidence in the absence of concrete facts. The prosecution persuaded the jury that Palmer was grossly in debt, had murdered his friend for his money and had covered his tracks by sabotaging the post mortem. Palmer's solicitor tried to procure a reprieve but this was refused. Palmer repeatedly professed that he was 'innocent of poisoning Cook by strychnine'. His brother, the Rev. Thomas Palmer, entreated him to confess if he was guilty but he replied, 'I have nothing to say, and nothing shall I say'.

On the morning of his execution, Palmer 'made his gallows toilet with serenity', denied the justice of his sentence and declared 'that he was a murdered man'.

Palmer's cell in Newgate Prison, where he awaited execution

WILLIAM WILLS 1834–1861

English explorer who shared the honour of being the first to cross Australia from south to north

William John Wills was a medical student at Bart's when he decided to emigrate to Australia. In his new country, he trained as a surveyor and went on to play a major role in a famous ill-fated expedition.

Born on 5 January 1835, William John Wills was a Devonshire boy from Totnes. His father, also called William, was the local doctor, and from an early age young William used to help out in the medical practice. On leaving St Andrew's Grammar School in Ashburton, he seemed set for the medical profession.

In 1852, Wills arrived in London and entered Bart's to attend Dr John Stenhouse's practical chemistry classes at the Medical School, where he excelled. His testimonial from Stenhouse read: 'He obtained considerable proficiency and invariably distinguished himself by great propriety of conduct'. By this time, however, his father had bought a share in the Melbourne Gold Mining Company and planned to go to Australia with his two eldest sons. Stenhouse begged Dr Wills not to take his son away from the medical school saying that he was one of the most promising pupils he had ever had.

The Burke and Wills expedition party set out from Melbourne amid great public excitement

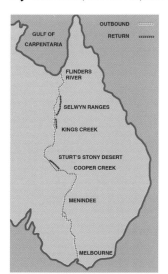

Map showing the route of the ill-fated expedition

Early days in Australia

Wills and his brother Thomas left Dartmouth on 1 October 1852 and arrived in Melbourne on 3 January 1853; their father followed nine months later. Wills had various temporary jobs before settling down to study surveying. In March 1859 he secured a permanent post at the Magnetic Observatory at Flagstaff Hill, working under the Government Meteorologist and Observatory Director.

Plans were already afoot to mount an expedition to find a route across the continent from the settled areas of Victoria to the Gulf of Carpentaria. Wills submitted himself as surveyor and astronomical and meteorological observer. He provided a reference from Richard Birnie which said, 'Wills is a thorough Englishman, self-relying and self-contained, a well-bred gentleman without a jot of effeminacy. Plucky as a mastiff, high bloodied as a racer, enterprising but reflective, cool, keen and as composed as daring. Few men talk less, few by manner and conduct, suggest more'. Wills was appointed third in command of the expedition on a salary of £300 a year. Robert O'Hara Burke was leader and George Landells second in command.

The expedition

The party that left Melbourne on 20 August 1860 for its planned 3,000 mile return journey, consisted of 19 men, 26 camels, 23 horses, six wagons and sufficient food for two years – as well as 270 litres of rum (apparently for medicinal purposes for the camels). Also included were a large bath tub, an oak and cedar table, a Chinese gong and 45 yards of gossamer for veils to protect against flies. Wills took a considerable amount of equipment as well as notebooks to record the expedition.

The going was slow and by the end of the first week only 60 miles had been covered but Wills was proving his worth by keeping detailed records and carrying out observations and tests. Before long there was trouble in the camp: Landells and Burke fell out and after Landells resigned Wills was promoted to second in command. At the beginning of October Burke and Wills left most of their men at a place called Menindee, and with a forward party of six men and 15 camels they pressed on to reach Cooper Creek on 11 November, an area unexplored by Europeans. The conditions were appalling, the heat unbearable and the flies dreadful, and frustratingly the rest of the party failed to catch up.

Burke split the party again and he, Wills and two others (John King and Charley Gray) formed the exploration party to Carpentaria, taking one horse and two camels. They set off on 16 December with minimum supplies and no tents. Wills continued to keep a series of diaries with concise reports of their progress. Temperatures were 50 degrees in the shade and while supplies lasted they ate salt beef stew with rice and bread, washed down with a cup of tea. The conditions worsened and on 10 February Wills and Burke left the other two and continued on foot, reaching the Gulf of Carpentaria the next day, their hard-earned mission accomplished.

Despair

Wills and Burke rejoined the others and started on the return journey but the party was hampered by the tropical monsoon downpours. Charley Gray died shortly before the group reached Cooper Creek on 21 April, where, to their great disappointment, they found the camp deserted. Wills noticed a message cut into a coolibah tree: DIG 3 FT W AP 21 (dig 3 ft west of the tree, April 21). On digging they found some supplies and a note explaining that the others had left just nine hours earlier. (It had been mutually agreed they would wait there for three months and 18 weeks had already passed.)

After burying Wills's notes and papers and a report from Burke, the three demoralised survivors left the next day but made little progress. They survived for several weeks on nardoo seed and fish given to them by friendly aborigines, but by late June Wills was very weak and they had completely run out of food. When Burke and King went in search of supplies, Wills wrote, 'Nothing now but the greatest good luck can save any of us'. This proved to be the final entry in his diary before he died, aged 27, alone, in the wilderness. Shortly afterwards, Burke also died, on about 28 June, leaving King as the sole survivor.

Public funeral

The bodies of Wills and Burke were recovered by a search party and subsequently lay in state for two weeks. On 21 January 1863 they received a state funeral when three quarters of the population of Melboune lined the streets to watch the procession. A monument was erected in Melbourne where it remains to this day and in Totnes an obelisk was erected alongside the house where Wills was born. It was generally agreed that it was 'only by his guidance and scientific talents that the great geographic success of the expedition was achieved'.

Despair for Wills and Burke beside the tree at Cooper Creek

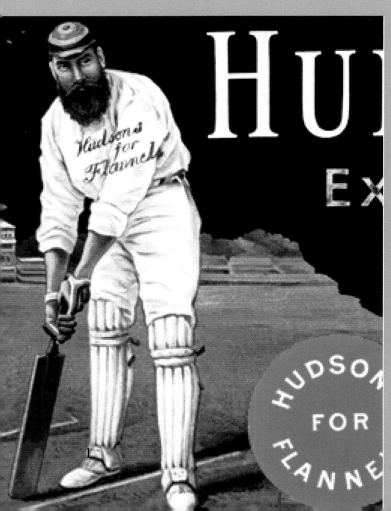

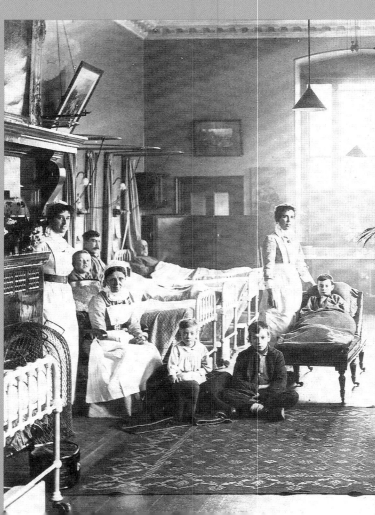

4

THE LATE VICTORIANS

At last women were beginning to make their mark in what was still very largely a bastion of male society. Elizabeth Blackwell was accepted as a postgraduate medical student at Bart's, and three educated, trained nurses became Matron: Maria Machin, who was not a success; Ethel Bedford Fenwick, the originator of the movement for state registered nurses; and Isla Stewart, who revolutionised nurse training. Bart's physician Dyce Duckworth was in favour of *ladies* becoming nurses but not doctors.

Aural surgeon, James Hinton, believed in the joys of sexual liberation and Edward Frankland was proud to report that London's water was excellent and wholesome. The need for hospital cleanliness was appreciated by George Rolleston during the Crimean War, but not by William Savory who thought Listerism was a waste of effort.

Jonathan Hutchinson, a surgeon honoured by the Royal College of Physicans, was against specialisation, whereas Thomas Smith was one of the earliest specialists at Bart's. Daniel Tuke, a Quaker, was a pioneer in the management of the insane, while Samuel Gee was the first to describe coeliac disease.

Medicine was not to the liking of all Bart's graduates. Henry 'Cavendish' Jones became a sports writer and was the inspiration behind the Wimbledon Lawn Tennis Championships. W.G. Grace, the cricketer, spent time as a medical student at Bart's when not scoring runs for his country.

ELIZABETH BLACKWELL 1821–1910

England's first 'lady doctor', a post-graduate at Bart's and a campaigner for women's rights

Elizabeth Blackwell, famous for her quest to become the first woman doctor in an English-speaking country, owed much of her success to the celebrated James Paget of Bart's.

Elizabeth Blackwell was born in Bristol on 3 February 1821, the third daughter in a family of nine children. Her father, Samuel, a sugar refiner and social reformist, believed in equality for his workers and for women, and felt that all his children, regardless of their sex, should be given the opportunity to develop their talents and abilities. Due to the state of the sugar business, the family left England for America when Elizabeth was aged 11 but unfortunately they fell upon hard times and Samuel died in 1838 leaving the family destitute. To

Lecture at the Women's Medical College, New York, established by Blackwell in 1868

support the family, Elizabeth and two of her sisters took over the running of a girls' school in Kentucky. Elizabeth hated teaching and was relieved when her brothers were old enough to become the family's breadwinners and the school was closed.

Elizabeth admitted being attracted to the opposite sex but found the thought of marriage and the prospect of spending a lifetime with a man daunting, and by the time she was 24 was looking for a new challenge. She visited a sick woman friend who was dying of a gynaecological condition who told her that if she had had a woman doctor she would have felt more comfortable. Apparently it was after this meeting that Elizabeth had the idea of pursuing a career in medicine.

Entry into medical college
Blackwell applied to 12 medical schools and was turned down by all of them – the male doctors thought women doctors were a good idea in principle but quite impossible in practice. The more Elizabeth was rejected, the more determined she

became. She wrote, 'The idea of winning a doctor's degree gradually assumed the aspect of a great moral struggle and the moral fight posed an immense attraction for me'.

At last she was accepted by Geneva University Medical College in New York State – where the faculty left it up to the 150 male students to accept or reject Blackwell's application, with the understanding that even if there was one vote against her admission she would be turned down. Thinking it was a practical joke, all the students voted in favour to admit her, and she started her studies in November 1847. It was not a happy time: half the students fell in love with her and the other half found her too clever. She graduated MD, top of the class, in 1849. However, reacting to the outrage of the medical profession, Geneva Medical College again closed its doors to women.

Bart's to the rescue
Blackwell decided to return to England to gain hospital experience, so she would become a

practically qualified doctor as well as a theoretically qualified one, but she failed to get a position. She enrolled instead at La Maternité, a midwifery school in Paris, under the condition that she would be treated as a student midwife. In 1849, while treating a baby with an eye infection, she spurted some contaminated solution into her own eye by accident and was blinded in one eye. Her hopes for a surgical career were over.

Meanwhile, Elizabeth Blackwell's cousin wrote round to London's teaching hospitals on Blackwell's behalf, and James Paget, who was dean at the time, responded warmly with the offer of a place at Bart's. Elizabeth later recalled the generous action of St Bartholomew's in aiding her entrance into the humane profession. In 1850 she took rooms at 28 Thavie's Inn and for 18 happy months spent the chief part of each day on the wards, where she found the doctors and nurses invariably friendly and helpful and her class of 60 male students 'very gentlemanly'. While she was at Barts she became friendly with the small group of women who were leading the campaign for woman's rights in England, and forged an alliance with Florence Nightingale. It was to Nightingale that Blackwell credited the view that sanitation was the supreme goal of medicine.

A WOMAN'S VIEW

'Well, we have our 'lady doctor' here at last and she has actually attended two of Sir James's lectures, taking her seat with perfect composure. The young men have behaved extremely well, and she appears likely to go on her way unmolested. ...Her manners are quiet and it is evident her motives for the pursuit of so strange a vocation are pure and good. So let us hope that she will become useful in her generation.'
Lydia Paget, wife of James Paget, October 1850

Medical career

Due to lack of funds and the worry that she would not be able to have a successful private practice in London, Elizabeth returned to America in 1851. There she struggled to find work until she and her sister Emily, now also a qualified doctor, opened a dispensary. Elizabeth returned to England in 1858 and her name was entered on the Medical Register of 1 January 1859. (From 1860 until 1876 the rules changed and no one without an English medical degree could register. This made it impossible for all women as the English universities still excluded women from admission.)

Blackwell again returned to America in 1861, and during the Civil War was responsible for training and despatching nurses to the war fronts. In 1868 she established a Women's Medical College in New York, and in 1869 she returned to England with the purpose of establishing medical education for women in England. She accepted the Chair

Stamp commemorating Blackwell's career, issued in the USA in 1974

of Gynaecology in 1875 at the newly established London School of Medicine but resigned due to ill health in 1877.

Later years

The remaining years of Blackwell's life were taken up with a mixture of causes, including moral reform, sexual purity, hygiene and medical education, preventive medicine and women's rights. She continued to reject woman's subservience to the male, but maintained that a woman's role was maternal and, although she never married, when she was 35 she adopted a seven-year-old orphan called Kitty. Elizabeth Blackwell died, aged 89, at her house in Hastings in 1910 after suffering a stroke.

JAMES HINTON 1822–1875

Social and sexual reformer lost to history

James Hinton, a Bart's-trained surgeon, was a philanthropic hedonist and passionate feminist who set out to influence the mid-Victorian concept of altruism in the slums of London.

SLUMMING

The term 'slumming' was first used to describe a practice in Victorian London whereby members of the upper and middle classes, often motivated by curiosity or a desire for adventure, visited areas populated by those of a lower socio-economic level. James Hinton was one of the trail-blazers.

The son of a Baptist minister, James Hinton was born in Reading in 1822. He was educated at his grandfather's school near Oxford and at a non-conformist school in Harpenden. Aged 16 he was apprenticed to a Whitechapel woollen draper but left after a year to become an insurance clerk. By the time he was 18 his increasing involvement with moral problems was affecting his health. He made plans to run away to sea, but on the advice of his doctor became a medical student at Bart's. After qualifying and a brief spell as an assistant surgeon in Essex, Hinton travelled as medical officer on a ship to Sierra Leone, where he looked after free labourers en route to Jamaica.

On returning to England in 1850 he became an aural surgeon. He married a couple of years later and he and his wife, Margaret, had several children. In 1863 he took a position at Guy's Hospital, where he acquired the reputation as a very skilful surgeon and was the first, with Hermann Schwartz, to develop the mastoid operation.

Hinton studied homeopathy and experimented with the placebo effect, believing that homeopathy worked via the patient's imagination. He held many unconventional ideas on psychology, philosophy and science, but freely admitted, 'My notions, though rather clever, may be the merest moonshine, no more likely to be true than cats walk on their tails'.

Slumming and reform

James Hinton dressed in plain, ill-fitting clothes and his manners were as unconventional as his morals. He became a friend to the poor, putting his interest down to his days as an apprentice when he witnessed the sexual degradation of working women. Hinton ached to live among the poor 'as a man longs for his wedding day'. He insisted that the rich could be fulfilled only by serving those in need, and he urged them to seek pleasure through altruism, which he believed would result in social and sexual freedom.

In his writings he promoted the sexual liberation of women and men in the slums of London, focusing exclusively on heterosexual activity. It seems he wanted to do good but to have pleasure at the same time. He disregarded sexual norms and, as a believer in free love, offered women, including his sister-in-law, the chance to experience the joys of sexual liberation with him. His followers included sexologist and social reformer Havelock Ellis and his wife (the lesbian Edith Lees); also Arnold Toynbee, in whose memory Toynbee Hall, a powerhouse of social reform, was named.

Hinton retired in 1874 and died a year later in the Azores, aged 53, of encephalitis. His virtual erasure from history was the result of a campaign of rumour and innuendo in the 1880s intended to discredit him and his ideas at precisely the time his supporters were trying to secure his reputation as a first-rate thinker and social visionary.

EDWARD FRANKLAND 1825–1899

Prestigious chemist, water analyst and discoverer of valency

After teaching chemistry at St Bartholomew's Medical College, Edward Frankland became one of the foremost chemists of his day. He had a particular interest in the water quality of Victorian London.

Born near Garstang, Lancashire, Edward Frankland was the illegitimate son of Peggy Frankland and a local lawyer. After attending a number of schools, including Lancaster Royal Grammar School, he was apprenticed at 15 to a druggist in Lancaster – but learnt little. Fortunately, he was able to perform experiments in his spare time, and in 1845 went to London to work in Lyon Playfair's laboratory at the Office of Woods and Forests. From 1847 to 1850 he studied in Germany, completing his doctorate under Robert Bunsen at the University of Marburg.

Lecturer in chemistry

Frankland moved back to England in 1850 to a post at Putney Civil Engineering College. In 1851 he became the first chemistry professor at what would become Manchester University. He was elected a Fellow of the Royal Society in 1853.

He returned to London in 1857 to teach chemistry at Bart's. Chemistry was clearly becoming more important for the study of disease. However, Frankland found that despite the emphasis on theoretical and organic chemistry in lectures at the Medical School, most of the practical work was limited. He believed that most chemical laboratories in England were 'adapted for beginners rather than for serious study' and that Bart's was no different – work was confined to examinations of urine, with little effort to examine blood or to train students how to do this. Frankland left Bart's in 1863.

Frankland was Professor of Chemistry at the Royal Institution from 1863 to 1868. He became Professor at the Royal College of Chemistry on a temporary basis in 1865, was given a permanent appointment in 1868 and stayed until 1885. He also taught for the 20 years from 1865 to 1885 at the Royal School of Mines.

Water expert

In 1868 Frankland was appointed a member of the second royal commission on the pollution of rivers. His main work involved water supply and he was provided with a laboratory from where he gave valuable information on the contamination of rivers and on water purification. He spent many hours devising more accurate methods of analysis, and made monthly reports on London's water until the end of his life – by which time he was convinced of its excellence and wholesomeness.

Edward Frankland was knighted in 1897 for his work on municipal water supplies. He was married twice and had two daughters. He died while on holiday in Norway in 1899.

CONTRIBUTIONS TO CHEMISTRY

Edward Frankland's contributions to chemistry were wide-ranging and important.

- He discovered valency – that 'the combining power of the attracting element is always satisfied with the same number of atoms'.
- He established a new branch of chemistry concerned with organo-metallic compounds.
- From observations on the summit of Mont Blanc, he realised that air pressure did not affect the rate of combustion of a candle but did affect a candle flame's luminosity.
- He made the first quantitive study of food combustion and the calorific values of foods.
- With Norman Lockyer, he discovered helium by means of spectroscopy.

WILLIAM SAVORY 1826–1895

Distinguished surgeon who declared against Listerism

William Savory rose from humble beginnings to gain high office at Bart's, at the Royal College of Surgeons and in the country. He was an academically gifted individual who rose to the top of his profession, but he failed to appreciate the need to avoid infection in surgery.

Born in Monument Court, on 30 November 1826, William Scovell Savory was proud to be a cockney. He was the son of William Henry Savory, a fish salesman (not a surgeon as some sources suggest), who died when William was a child. William and his younger brother, Charles Tozer Savory (who also became a doctor, graduating MD from St Andrews), were brought up by their mother and apparently received a private education, perhaps paid for by the Company of Fishmongers.

Savory's baptismal record showing his father's occupation

William, who was clearly extremely bright, entered St Bartholomew's Hospital in 1844, aged 18. He was admitted a member of the Royal College of Surgeons in 1847 and graduated MB from the University of London in 1848, having won all the gold medals, in comparative anatomy and physiology, surgery, and midwifery, as well as honours in medicine.

Student unrest
Shortly after qualification, William Savory was appointed demonstrator of anatomy and operative surgery at the Medical School of Bart's, and in 1850 he was considered an ideal choice for the post of tutor to supervise the studies of students reading for degrees in the University of London. In 1852 he was elected Fellow of the Royal College of Surgeons, and in 1859 took over from James Paget as lecturer on general anatomy and physiology and curator of the Bart's museum.

True to form, the students were an unruly bunch and there was uproar when an ardent feminist, Miss Ellen Colbourne, was accepted into the Medical School in 1865. Her time at Bart's, however, was short-lived. During one of his lectures, in an attempt to quell the usual mayhem, Savory asked the students to vote if, under the circumstances, they wished 'the *lady*' to remain. Only two voted for her to stay. She could stand the 'hooting and the screaming no longer' and took her leave forever.

Having been elected assistant surgeon in 1862, Savory was made full surgeon at Bart's in 1867. Two years later, he became joint lecturer in surgery, and then, at the special request of his colleagues, had sole occupancy of this post from 1879 to 1889.

The meeting at Cork
William Savory upheld the great surgical traditions of Bart's, which taught that 'each should act to the best of their ability, be scrupulously honest in word and deed, fear no one and act together for the institution'. However, although Savory was a great surgeon of the old school, he had his limitations and resisted the new advances in surgery.

He was a born orator and, at a meeting of the British Medical Association at Cork in 1879, he gave a controversial but polite address against Listerism. He saw Lister's approach of promoting scrupulous cleanliness and use of carbolic acid spray during surgery as a waste of time and effort. This address by Savory was described as the last public expression by a prominent surgeon against the by then widely accepted method of modern surgery. Undaunted, on his return to Bart's, Savory apparently teased his 'pro antisepsis' colleagues and was said to have excluded from his wards any house surgeon who smelt of antiseptics.

Bart's and beyond

Savory was a popular, well-liked man with a strong personality. He was known for never raising his voice or losing his temper and had a habit of scratching his right ear when he was pleased or puzzled. He was considered an excellent and just examiner and was sufficiently sarcastic to be a terror to the idle and the ignorant. As lecturer in surgery he was a fitting successor to Abernethy, Lawrence and Paget. His income from Bart's in

A miniature replica of William Savory's bust at the RCS – given to people who contributed funds to commission the original

1880–1881 was probably the largest ever received for surgical teaching. In 1891, aged 65, he resigned as lecturer to become consultant surgeon and governor of the hospital.

William Savory was elected a Fellow of the Royal Society in 1851. At the Royal College of Surgeons, he was Hunterian Professor of Comparative Anatomy and Physiology from 1859 to 1861, a member of the court of examiners from 1870 to 1884, became a member of council in 1877, was Vice President in 1883 and 1884, and President for four years, from 1885 to 1888. He was appointed Surgeon Extraordinary to Queen Victoria in 1887 and was made a baronet in 1890.

William Savory had a happy domestic life, marrying his wife Louisa Frances Borradaile in 1854. They had an only son, Borradaile, who became rector of St Bartholomew the Great. William lived for many years in Mayfair, London but named his baronetcy for The Woodlands, Buckinghamshire, his country house at Stoke Poges. He remained true to his cockney roots – and happily dropped his aitches until the day he died.

LISTERISM:
Discovery and acceptance

In 1861 Joseph Lister, Professor of Surgery at Glasgow University, was concerned about the level of cleanliness in operating theatres. He believed a 'poisonous miasma' (bad smells in the air) might cause wounds to turn septic.

In 1865 he learned of Pasteur's work on microbes and realised that germs in the air and on surgical dressings might be causing infection. He carried out an experiment on 11-year-old James Greenlees who had a compound fracture of his tibia. Lister cleaned the wound and dressed it in a bandage soaked in carbolic acid. The dressing stayed in place for four days and remained infection free – and the boy walked out of the infirmary six weeks later.

By 1867 Lister knew that germs were always in the air and could get into the wound during surgery. He developed an antiseptic ritual that included use of his own invention, the carbolic acid spray – with which he managed to saturate all those present. Later, he abandoned the spray as he found that germs carried on fingers, dressings and the skin of the patient were a more important cause of infection than those in the air.

What came to be known as Listerian principles were adopted by surgeons in many countries and Joseph Lister has come to be known as the 'father of antiseptic surgery'.

DANIEL HACK TUKE 1827–1895

Cool-eyed observer of nature who became one of the most important psychiatrists of his day

Daniel Hack Tuke was a prominent campaigner for the humane treatment of the insane. His careful observations and literary ability also made him famous as a compiler of information on mental health.

Born in York on 19 April 1827, Daniel Hack Tuke was the 13th child of Samuel Tuke, a psychiatrist and humanitarian reformer. The Tukes were a family of philanthropic York Quakers, whose money came from cocoa, chocolate and tea. Daniel's great grandfather, William Tuke, founded The Retreat in York, an asylum for the mentally ill.

Daniel was a delicate child and it was felt that he would be more suited to law than business. He was therefore articled to a solicitor, but this was not a success and his health suffered from the 'drudgery of copying papers'. Instead, he went to work with his father at The Retreat and was made Steward.

The Retreat, founded in 1796, was based on Quaker principles and famously pioneered the humane and moral treatment of patients with mental disturbance. Physical punishment was banned, manacles were not used and there was no restraint using chains. The treatment was based on restoring self-esteem and self-control. It was while working there that Daniel decided to study medicine.

In 1850 he moved to London to study at Bart's, and became the first pupil to attend lectures at the Hanwell Lunatic Asylum, which was the first purpose-built asylum in England and Wales. He obtained his MRCS diploma in 1852.

Travels and appointments

After receiving his MD in Heidelberg in 1853, Tuke with his new wife, Esther, toured Europe visiting asylums. It would appear that this trip was the start of his careful collection of observations. At the asylum in Siegburg in Prussia he saw five men and eight women restrained by strait waistcoat or coercion chair. He reported his findings to his father and wrote, 'I could not but contrast the noise with, and the expressions of the patients with the comparative quiet of the Hanwell Asylum where there are 1,000 patients compared with 190'.

On his return to England, Tuke became assistant physician to The Retreat as well as physician to the York Dispensary. During this time he made detailed records of patients' histories and case notes. In 1859, after a pulmonary haemorrhage, he gave up work and went to live in Falmouth for 15 years. Happily, he returned to good health and in 1875 he settled in London. He was elected a Fellow of the Royal College of Physicians, and became a specialist in mental disease at Charing Cross Hospital and a trustee of the Bethlem Hospital. In 1881 he became President of the Medico-Psychological Association.

Literary work

Daniel Hack Tuke wrote many books, including, with Dr John Bucknill, *The Manual of Psychological Medicine,* published in 1878 and for many years the standard work on insanity. In 1880 he became joint editor of *The Journal of Mental Science* (now *The British Journal of Psychiatry*). He also edited the *Dictionary of Psychological Medicine*, the most ambitious British psychiatric work of the 19th century. He died on 5 March 1895 aged 67.

CHAMPION OF HUMANE TREATMENT FOR THE MENTALLY ILL

Daniel Hack Tuke, true to his Quaker principles, was a strong opponent of the then common use of coercion devices and physical punishment for people with mental health problems.

GEORGE ROLLESTON 1829–1881

Physician at Smyrna during the Crimean War and the first Linacre Professor at Oxford University

George Rolleston became a medical student at Bart's after studying classics at Oxford. He was a protégé of Thomas Huxley, the evolutionary biologist.

Young George was the son of George Rolleston, the vicar and squire of Maltby in Yorkshire. He was first taught by his father and then attended Gainsborough Grammar School and the Collegiate School in Sheffield before gaining an open scholarship to Pembroke College, Oxford in 1846.

It was no surprise that Rolleston obtained a first class degree, in classics, and in 1851 he was elected to a fellowship, established by a Mrs Sheppard, for the promotion of the study of law and physic. This award inspired Rolleston to enter the medical profession and he spent his next three years at Bart's.

The Crimean War

Rolleston qualified in 1854 and was appointed to be a physician at the British Civil Hospital in Smyrna

The British hospital in Smyrna during the Crimean War

(now Izmir) during the final stages of the Crimean War. He took great interest in the hospital's sanitary aspects and at the end of the war wrote the *Report on Smyrna*. The historian A.W. Kinglake described the hospital as 'a model of what can be done for the care of troops sick and wounded'. Interestingly, much to Florence Nightingale's dismay, the nurses appointed to work at Smyrna did not come under her jurisdiction.

On returning home Rolleston spent a short time at Great Ormond Street Hospital before being appointed physician at the Radcliffe Infirmary, Oxford in 1857. Three years later he became the

first Linacre Professor of Anatomy and Physiology at Oxford, a position which he held until his death.

Rolleston was charismatic, inspirational and supportive. He was also full of energy, switching rapidly between interests. His friend, William Savory, felt that 'he touched many things, and most of them with effect, but he produced nothing worthy fully of himself. He was far greater than he appeared to be in any work he has left behind'.

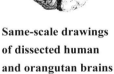

The famous meeting

Rolleston was present at the historic meeting of the British Association at the Oxford University Museum in 1860, often referred to as 'one of the great stories of the history of science'. Darwin's recently published book, *On the Origin of Species,* was the subject of a debate between Richard Owen and Thomas Huxley, a supporter of Darwin. They came to blows with reference to the structural differences between the brains of men and apes. This led Rolleston to set to work studying brain development and skull classification in man and animals. Subsequently, at a meeting in Cambridge in 1862, when Owen renewed his dispute with Huxley, Rolleston supported Huxley.

Same-scale drawings of dissected human and orangutan brains

Rolleston was involved in university politics and in many affairs of Oxford city, including helping to initiate the mains drainage. He was elected a Fellow of the Royal College of Physicians in 1859 and a Fellow of the Royal Society in 1862. Grace Harvey became his wife in 1861 and they had seven children, including three sons who became physicians. On 16 June 1881 Rolleston died of kidney failure at the young age of 51.

JONATHAN HUTCHINSON 1828–1913

Brilliant but humourless generalist, who was totally obstinate in his convictions

Jonathan Hutchinson was a surgeon who also had a keen interest in dermatology, ophthalmology and venereology. He was a committed generalist who opposed specialisation.

Born in Selby, Yorkshire on 23 July 1828, Jonathan Hutchinson was the second child and second son among his Quaker parents' 12 children. In his early professional life Hutchinson gave up the outward appearance of Quakerism but religion continued to be important to him. His father, also Jonathan, was a well-to-do middleman in the flax trade and young Jonathan was encouraged to enjoy farming activities. With his siblings, he was educated first at home and then at a local day school. At 17, he was apprenticed to Caleb Williams, an apothecary and surgeon in York, and after five years went to London to continue his medical studies at Bart's.

A tall, dark, solemn young man, Hutchinson studied under James Paget, who apparently was his inspiration. In 1850 he became a member of the Royal College of Surgeons, but failed to be elected to the staff at Bart's. Still hoping for a hospital appointment, Hutchinson fought against going into private practice and instead made a meagre living from medical journalism and teaching. However, having struggled to make ends meet, he put up his

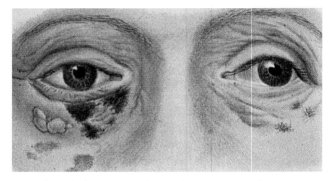

Hutchinson's freckle (lentigo maligna melanoma)

surgeon's plate at 14 Finsbury Circus in 1856, the year he married Jane West, with whom he would have 10 children.

Hospital appointments

Hutchinson was appointed assistant surgeon to The London Hospital in 1859, when he was 31, and became full surgeon there in 1863. Over the years, he also practised at Moorfields Eye Hospital, the London Lock Hospital (which specialised in venereology), the City of London Chest Hospital, the Metropolitan Free Hospital and the Blackfriars Hospital for Diseases of the Skin. He was known to be a painstaking and accurate observer as well as an assiduous note taker, and his clinical knowledge was considered to be second to none.

Among Hutchinson's other skills was an ability to teach. His incredible memory and clarity of thought attracted many to attend his lectures on numerous different subjects. He was described as being very severe in appearance, with a long beard and dark eyes peering through his spectacles (four pairs of which he always carried on his person). He addressed his audience 'in precise clear-cut sentences, rather solemn, without much sparkle, but full of meat'.

Due to his obvious success and enthusiasm for spreading knowledge, Hutchinson decided to

---

**EPONYMS FOR
JONATHAN HUTCHINSON**

Hutchinson's angina; Hutchinson's disease; Hutchinson's dyshidrosis; Hutchinson's facies; Hutchinson's freckle; Hutchinson's mask; Hutchinson's melanotic disease; Hutchinson's patch; Hutchinson's potato tumour; Hutchinson's prurigo; Hutchinson's pupil; Hutchinson's sign; Hutchinson's teeth; Hutchinson's triad; Hutchinson-Boeck syndrome; Hutchinson-Gilford progeria syndrome establish a postgraduate school. In 1883, at his own expense, he opened a Clinical Museum at 1 Park Crescent. This transferred in 1898 to 22 Chenies Street, on which building a notice was placed stating: 'The Medical Graduate College and Polyclinic; lectures to be given at 5.15 p.m.'.

Although this initiative has been considered to herald London's Postgraduate Medical School, Hutchinson's establishment was always in financial trouble and only survived during his lifetime. It failed because it had no associate hospital where teaching could be based on clinical and laboratory investigation.

Generalist par excellence

Jonathan Hutchinson's documentation of his original clinical observations and understanding of how diseases were caused, have made him a key contributor to dermatology and medicine in general. This is reflected in the

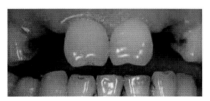

Hutchinson's teeth, with notches, a sign of congenital syphilis

fact that Hutchinson's name continues with more eponyms than that of any other individual.

Perhaps he is best known for his work on syphilis. In the days before the Wasserman test, Hutchinson provided the means to provide a firm diagnosis based on his triad of notched incisor teeth, labyrinthine deafness and interstitial keratitis. He was, however, incorrect on the cause of leprosy. He firmly maintained that the disease was caused by the consumption of decaying and contaminated fish. His book *Leprosy and fish eating* was published in 1906.

From 1889 to 1900, Hutchinson was honorary secretary to the New Sydenham Society, which published the journal *Archives of Surgery.* During the 11 years of its existence Hutchinson was the sole contributor, and when the journal was reviewed by the *British Medical Journal* it was suggested by the reviewer that, as all the articles were written by Mr Hutchinson, why were they not named 'Mr Hutchinson's Archives'? The illustrations in the *Archives* were beautifully executed by a Mr Edwin Burgess and in 1891 a collection of the original drawings was offered to the Royal College of Surgeons, but not accepted.

Elections and awards

Hutchinson was elected FRCS in 1862 and President of the College in 1889. However, he stepped down from this position after only one year instead of the usual four, an action thought to be due to the refusal of the College to buy his collection of drawings by Burgess. Hutchinson was elected a Fellow of the Royal Society in 1882 and President of the London International Dermatological Congress in 1896. It was at this congress that he astutely remarked, 'If we ask how the most rapid development has come about the answer must be: by the aid of cheap printing and cheap travelling. We are now able to communicate easily with one another and to make mental use of each other's brains.'

Hutchinson, like many other medical men and lawyers, was caricatured by 'Spy'

He received many honorary degrees but must have been most proud when he was awarded the Moxon Medal of the Royal College of Physicians for 'his long and valuable services to clinical medicine' – this was the first time that a Fellow of the Royal College of Surgeons had been honoured in this way. Jonathan Hutchinson was knighted in 1908 for distinguished service to medicine. He died on 23 June 1913.

HENRY 'CAVENDISH' JONES 1831–1899

Anyone for tennis? Doctor who gave up medicine to write on games and sports

Henry Jones was disenchanted with medicine and decided to take a change of direction. Tennis lovers have him to thank for the popular summer event held each year on the lush green grass in London SW19 – the Wimbledon Lawn Tennis Championships.

After entering Bart's as a medical student in 1849, Henry Jones went on to take his MRCP and to become a GP. However, he grew disillusioned with general practice and so decided to become a full-time writer on games and sports, which was much more to his liking.

A member of the famous Cavendish whist club,

A book by 'Cavendish'

Henry was an expert at the game and wrote articles on it before writing his first book, *The Laws and Principles of Whist*, which appeared in 1862. These principles were explained by 'Cavendish' – the nom de plume by which Henry became famous. His writing career blossomed with further books on other card games, billiards, croquet and lawn tennis as well as many articles for *The Field*, the original country and field sports magazine, and contributions to the *Encyclopaedia Britannica*.

Henry Jones joined the newly founded All England Croquet Club in 1869 and, as a committee member, in 1875 proposed that one of the croquet lawns be set aside for playing lawn tennis as the finances of

An idyllic game of croquet

the club were in dire straits. This was agreed and he and two others formed a sub-committee to frame the rules of lawn tennis, many of which remain today. Two years later 'Lawn Tennis' was included in the Club's official title and then in 1882 the word 'Croquet' was quietly dropped (though reinstated later). A problem with the pony roller for tending the courts in 1877 led the sub-committee members to come up with the idea of holding a tennis tournament to raise money for the repair: the Wimbledon Championships at Worple Road were born!

Henry was to be a referee at the championships from 1877 to 1885. The number of events was to increase but in the first year the only event was the Gentlemen's Singles. Twenty-two competitors took part in the contest, each paying a guinea entry fee, and the 200 spectators were all charged one shilling to attend. Spencer Gore was the champion, beating William Marshall in the final. The latter, smarting from defeat, was unimpressed with the new game

Victorian wooden tennis racquet and net of balls

and said it would never catch on. A profit of £10 was made from the event, which was ample to repair the roller.

When Henry Jones died in 1899 the fortunes at Wimbledon were again dwindling and affection for the championships had fallen away during the 1890s. Sadly, in his obituaries no reference was made to his important role in the establishment of the most famous tennis championships in the world.

THOMAS SMITH 1833–1909

Colourful, compassionate man who always tried to do the right thing for his patients

The surgeon Thomas Smith was one of the earliest specialists at Bart's and the first consulting surgeon at Great Ormond Street Hospital.

Thomas, the sixth son of Benjamin Smith, was born at Blackheath on 23 March 1833. His father, a goldsmith, sent Thomas to Tonbridge School, but bankruptcy followed and it was only due to Benjamin's friendship with James Paget that Thomas became, in 1851, one of the last of the hospital apprentices at Bart's. He was not studious, and claimed never to have opened a book on surgery until *after* he had passed his MRCS in 1854.

On qualification Smith became a house surgeon at Great Ormond Street Hospital for Children but knee trouble forced him to leave. However, he was able to assist Paget and to tutor pupils, resulting in 1859 in the publication of his *Manual of Operative Surgery on the Dead Body.* Fully recovered, he became Demonstrator of Anatomy and Teacher of Operative Surgery at Bart's in 1859.

Smith was made assistant surgeon at Bart's in 1864 and was placed in charge of the Aural Department, one of the hospital's first specialist departments. He was full surgeon at Bart's from 1873 until 1898, as well as being assistant surgeon, surgeon and then consulting surgeon at Great Ormond Street, and also surgeon to the Alexandra Hospital for Children with Hip Disease in Bloomsbury.

Skilled operator

Thomas Smith operated with speed and safety. He was famous for the repair of cleft palate and hare lip and developed the tubular cleft-palate needle and Smith's mouth gag. Users of the gag were advised to use chloroform, as 'the operation may be performed with

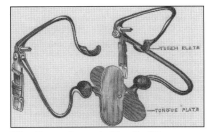

Mouth gag invented by Smith

far greater rapidity and precision than when the surgeon is dependent upon the self-control of even the most courageous patient'.

Smith famously also experimented on dogs, using horse hair rather than wire for suturing wounds. On one occasion, a sutured, well chloroformed dog apparently died and was thrown away. The next morning the dog was standing on the doorstep waiting to be let in!

Unlike many senior colleagues at Bart's, Smith was an early convert to Listerism. He was reputed to have extracted a stone from the bladder of a child in 13 seconds, but nonetheless was one of the first to use the lithotrite.

At least one laboratory dog soon recovered

Personal matters

Thomas Smith married in 1862, but sadly his wife, Ann Parbury, died shortly after the birth of their ninth child. In her memory, Smith set up what was to become the Parbury Smith Maternity Fund at Bart's. He devoted himself to his large family and declined to be put forward for the office of President of the Royal College of Surgeons.

Smith was made Surgeon-Extraordinary to Queen Victoria in 1895, became a baronet in 1897, helped found a home for officers wounded in the Boer War, and in 1901 was made KCVO. In 1901 he became honorary Serjeant-Surgeon to Edward VII – and assisted at the King's appendicectomy on the day planned for the Coronation, 24 June 1902.

Thomas Smith was well loved. He delighted his young patients at Great Ormond Street by deliberately sliding along Sister's highly polished floors. He was a humble man devoted to duty and to his family. He died on 1 October 1909.

SAMUEL GEE 1839–1911

Describer of coeliac disease and the originator of Gee's Linctus

Samuel Gee was one of the first appointees to Bart's to come from outside the hospital. His description of coeliac disease in 1887 was the first to be given since ancient times.

The Bart's Fountain has always been an attraction to staff and patients alike

A Londoner born and bred, Samuel Gee lived as a child above his father William's china shop in Oxford Street. From an early age, Samuel proved clever and hardworking.

He was educated at home and then at University College School before studying medicine at University College Hospital from 1857 to 1861. He gained his MD and MRCP in 1865, and was elected a fellow in 1870.

Gee became a house surgeon at Great Ormond Street Hospital, where he came to the attention of Thomas Smith, who had a position there and also at Bart's. Smith put in a good word for Gee at Bart's, and thanks to his patronage Gee was able to secure a position as assistant physician there while continuing at the children's hospital.

In 1869 Gee was put in charge of the skin department at Bart's, although he derided the image of any form of specialism. He then became demonstrator in morbid anatomy and lecturer in pathological anatomy. From 1878 to 1893 he held the post of physician, and then was consulting physician until he retired in 1904. From 1901 to 1904 he was physician to the Prince of Wales.

Teacher, writer and diagnostician

Samuel Gee was a very popular teacher although he was quite shy. His motto was 'Thrift in words' and he would issue short pithy observations, which were imitated, along with his way of speech, by his students. It is said that he taught a five-year-old how to tell his visitors what was wrong with him, and the child proudly reported, 'Hydronephrosis, from the Greek words hudor, water and nephros, kidney'.

Gee wrote two best sellers: *Auscultation and Percussion* and *Lectures and Aphorisms*. His publications were based on observations, both clinical and from corpses (gleaned from his favourite occupation in the post mortem room). Today, Gee is perhaps best remembered as the originator of Gee's Linctus, a cough suppressant containing opium and oxymal of squill. He is also known for identifying and describing coeliac disease, making the observation that 'If the patient can be cured at all it must be by means of diet'

Gee linked coeliac disease with diet

The man

Samuel Gee was sartorially elegant. He wore the orthodox frock coat and tall hat of the Victorian consultant and would be driven into the Square in a brougham drawn by a pair of grey horses. His best friend was Robert Bridges, the poet, who was a colleague and had been Gee's best man on his marriage to Sarah Cooper in 1875. Bridges wrote a short poem in Latin about him, the translation of which gives a glimpse into Gee the mentor: 'But who is this coming, slender and sleek haired, following the big men, himself half as tall? Is it you, Gee? Had you not been my guide, philosopher and friend, the learned school of medicine would be jeering at my headlong retreat'.

Gee died from a coronary occlusion in August 1911 while on holiday in the Lake District. Appropriately, he left instructions for a post mortem to be performed on his body.

DYCE DUCKWORTH 1840–1928

Physician who was in favour of 'ladies' becoming nurses – but not doctors

Dyce Duckworth is remembered as a distinguished figure in the medical world of Victorian London and was a fine example of the cultured physicians of the time.

The fourth and youngest son of Liverpool merchant Robinson Duckworth and his wife Elizabeth, Dyce Duckworth was born and grew up in that city. He attended the Royal Institution School before moving on to Edinburgh University, where he graduated MB in 1862. The following year he proceeded to MD and was awarded the gold medal for his thesis.

Duckworth decided not to remain in Edinburgh but went south to London and to St Bartholomew's Hospital to continue his studies. Shortly after his arrival, he saw there was no likelihood of a post for him at the hospital and therefore left to join the Royal Navy as assistant surgeon. Within a year, however, due to unexpected deaths and resignations, he returned to Bart's as medical tutor. He was elected assistant physician in 1869, served as full physician from 1883 to 1896, and finally was made consulting physician in 1906. From 1890 to 1901 he was physician to the Prince of Wales, the future Edward VII.

The Royal College of Physicians

Undoubtedly the Royal College of Physicians played a large role in Duckworth's life. He was elected

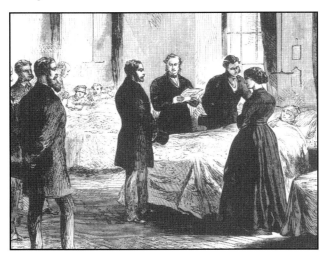

The Prince of Wales on a Bart's ward visit in 1868

member in 1865 and fellow in 1870, and served as councillor, examiner, censor and senior censor. He became treasurer in 1884, a post he held for 39 years, only retiring in 1923 when he was elected emeritus treasurer. He never became president.

Duckworth delivered many lectures at the College, including the Harveian Oration in 1898 during which he expounded on his favourite subject, 'the influence of character and right judgement in medicine'. He was an exponent of the art of medicine and feared this would be lost in the effort to make medicine into an exact science. It is considered that he diagnosed himself when he said 'a great physician is, and must be, a great artist'.

Views on women

It would appear that Duckworth supported the new breed of lady probationer nurses and in 1888 he became vice president of the newly formed Royal British Nurses Association. His view was that the public did not understand the position of a well educated, trained nurse. As far as he was concerned, however, he told a gathering of probationer nurses in 1895 that 'their job was to carry out the doctor's orders with implicit obedience and exactitude; and if [a nurse] has any opinions, she should keep them to herself'.

He could not imagine that any decent woman would wish to study medicine and he disliked the intrusion of women into the medical profession, maintaining that the proper place for them was at home or, at most, as nurses.

Dyce Duckworth was knighted in 1886. He was a Tory, an Anglican and a good churchman, very much a traditionalist, part of the medical elite and a stickler for etiquette. However, he was laborious, pompous and meticulous and apparently drove his assistants to distraction. He was twice married and died at the age of 87 after years of ill health.

MARIA MACHIN 1843–1905

The first Bart's Matron who had trained as a nurse

Maria Machin had every good reason to be reticent in taking up the post of Matron and Superintendent of Nurses at Bart's; she lasted only two years, from December 1878 to January 1881.

Maria Machin was born in Canada, in Sherbrooke, Ontario, and was brought up in Quebec. After spending several years running a girls' school, Machin decided she wanted to train as a nurse. As this was not possible in Canada at the time, she went first to Germany and then, in 1872, to the Nightingale School at St Thomas's Hospital in London. As a new probationer nurse, Machin heard Florence Nightingale give her rallying cry: 'to be a good nurse, one must be an improving woman; for stagnant waters sooner or later, always grow corrupt and unfit for use. Is any one of us a stagnant woman?'

Machin's training lasted for a mere nine months during which she was ill for 53 days and suffered from a septic finger which reduced the time she spent nursing on the wards. Despite her ill health she was obviously considered worthy and went on for a brief period to become the Nurses' Home Sister at St Thomas's, being known at the time as 'the most spiritual of the Nightingales'.

Canada experiment

In 1874 the Committee of Management at the Montreal General Hospital resolved that 'a system of trained hospital nurses such as was approved in England should be introduced'. They contacted the Council of the Nightingale Fund who agreed to provide support and to send Machin to Canada as Lady Superintendent. It was understood that the Montreal Hospital was to be re-built and replaced with a new, model hospital; Nightingale, who had a passion for designing hospitals, was most enthusiastic. However, she seems not to have learnt that plans are one thing, money and execution are another – and the proposed new hospital never materialised.

Machin was keen to return to Canada, and in 1875 set off happily to her homeland taking four nurses with her. Within a year, though, one of the nurses

NIGHTINGALE FUND

The Nightingale School at St Thomas's owed its existence to the Nightingale Fund, launched in 1857 to give the British public an opportunity to show their appreciation of the heroic efforts of Florence Nightingale and her band of nurses during the Crimean War (1854–1856). The Fund's purpose was 'to establish a permanent institution for the training, sustenance and protection of nurses and to arrange their proper instruction and employment'.

had died of typhoid, one had married and one was 'too educated' to cope, but the fourth turned out to be invaluable. Meanwhile, Machin became engaged to Dr Jack Cline and began reforming many of the nursing practices. She appealed for more nurses to be sent from England but, as all plans for re-building the hospital had been dropped, Nightingale's interest in the hospital declined and she refused the request. The Montreal Committee complained that Machin's work was not only increasing costs but that she had failed to establish a training school. Machin's marriage plans were dashed when her fiancé died of diphtheria, and, although the Montreal experiment lasted another year, she and her team of nurses resigned from their posts in 1878 and returned to England.

Matron at Bart's

After the resignation of Frances Drake as Matron of Bart's in 1878, the Governors approached the Nightingale Fund Committee to help them find a trained nurse who would be a suitable candidate to replace her. They recommended Maria Machin and provided an excellent reference, reporting that she was of 'altogether superior education' and 'unflinching in resolution'. Machin, herself, was very unsure, as her experience in Montreal had left her feeling that she was unsuitable for a managerial role. It was suggested that she should have a trial period before making a final decision but on reflection she decided against this and agreed to take the post in December 1878 when she was 37.

Still very much relying on the support of Nightingale, Machin was keen to instil the principles of the Nightingale School and she appointed some of the Sisters who had returned with her from Canada to fill vacant Sisters' posts at Bart's. She was keen to rush through changes at the hospital, and in 1879 she complained that she had been able to change little in her first year of employment. However, she had managed to raise the minimum age for probationers from 20 to 23 years and had increased the length of training from one to two years. The salary for first year probationers was reduced from £10 to £8 and second year probationers were paid £12 a year.

A tender scene by the Fountain – a nurse with a sick baby

Machin was supported by William Savory, who felt she had improved the character of the probationary nurses and that their work was more satisfactory. James Paget said that, 'the changes already made for the better, are far more than can have been expected ten or fifteen years ago'. This astute man did, however, warn of possible problems if Machin tried to change things too quickly.

By November 1879, she was becoming frustrated. She wrote that the hospital authorities 'prefer gradual improvement to radical reforms' and she grumbled that the Treasurer was never available to see her. She knew she was not a natural leader: she was not good with her staff, who were obstructive, and she could not persuade the untrained Sisters to change their traditional ways of working.

Resignation

Maria Machin resigned in January 1881 after only a brief period as Matron. It was apparent she was really not cut out for the job. She had a deep conviction that her calling was a religious one and she wanted to nurse the sick rather than govern nurses who were well. She went on to fulfil her vocational desire by joining the Bishop of Bloemfontein as a missionary nurse in South Africa. In 1884 she married Walter Redpath, an Englishman with business interests in South Africa. She later returned to nursing for financial reasons and to support British efforts in the Boer War (1899–1902).

NIGHTINGALE'S NOTES ON NURSING

Florence Nightingale's book, *Notes on Nursing: what it is and what it is not*, published in 1859, included advice and practices for:
- Ventilation and warming
- Health in houses
- Noise
- Taking food
- Bed and bedding
- Cleanliness of rooms
- Personal cleanliness
- Observation of the sick

'The greatest cricketer England has ever seen'

William Gilbert Grace (generally known as W.G. Grace) completed part of his medical training at St Bartholomew's Hospital. While continuing his studies he still managed completely to dominate the first-class game of cricket.

Born of a cricket-mad family, it was perhaps W.G. Grace's destiny that he would follow in the footsteps of his relatives. No fewer than 14 family members had played first-class cricket and two of his brothers went on to play Test cricket for England.

Gilbert, or Willie as he was called by his mother, was born on 18 July 1848 at Downend House, Downend, near Bristol. When he was barely two years old he was already wielding the bat, and the whole family, which included his four older sisters, his three older brothers and a younger brother and the dogs (who, with the girls, just fielded) all played the game.

W.G. was notoriously unscholarly. He attended the village school until he was 14 and then went to

> **ENTRANCE TO CRICKET GROUND**
>
> *Admission 6d*
> *If W.G. Grace plays:*
> *Admission 1 shilling*
>
> **Spectators often had to pay a premium to see their hero.**

a day school before being home schooled by the Downend village parish curate. However, he always preferred being out of doors, living the life of a country boy, when one of his main activities was throwing stones at birds in the fields – which, he said, was the source of his skill as an outfielder.

Medical training

Grace's father was the local doctor and he was keen for W.G., in common with his other three sons, to follow in the family tradition. As a result of his prowess at cricket, it was not surprising in those days that W.G. was approached by a member of Oxford University Cricket Club in 1866, and then by Caius College, Cambridge in 1868, to attend their university as an undergraduate (and ensure their cricketing success). Grace went to neither and instead enrolled at Bristol Medical School in 1868, when he was 20. He then began a very long training period during which time he was in his prime as a cricketer and managed to include two overseas tours.

W.G. completed his training at Bart's and the Westminster Hospital after he and his family moved to London in 1875. His final year was spent at the Westminster but he is said to have owed his success in his final exams to coaching from Howard Marsh of Bart's. In November 1879, aged 31, he qualified as Licentiate of the

While technically an amateur, W.G. Grace made plenty of money from his sport

Royal College of Physicians (LRCP) and Member of the Royal College of Surgeons (MRCS).

Cricketing success

No single English cricketer to this day has dominated the game as totally as Grace did over his more than 40 years of playing first-class cricket from 1865 to 1908. He took 2,876 first-class wickets and scored 54,896 runs. He captained England, Gloucestershire County Cricket Club, the Gentlemen, the MCC, the United South of England Eleven and several other teams. His participation in a match guaranteed to add thousands to the crowd. He was no saint and was quick to become embroiled in confrontations, both on and off the field, but he swiftly made up and tended to regret his actions. The commonest adverse perception from others was that

W.G. Grace early in his career

he was a cheat and he bent the rules to suit himself.

Although Grace was amateur in name and by nature he approached each match in a professional manner, and apparently earned more money from the game than any of the so-called professionals at the time. Apart from his roles as secretary and manager of the London County Club for which he was paid, he also featured in advertisements and was the recipient of the proceeds of two national testimonial matches as well as an allowance of £36 15s per annum to pay for locum assistants who covered his medical duties.

General Practice

The other side of W.G. Grace's character showed itself when he became a family physician in Bristol in 1879. His was a mixed practice and undoubtedly W.G. was popular with all his patients and provided many acts of kindness to the less well off. He had a soft heart and poor families knew they did not need to worry about calling him out as the bill would never arrive. It has been suggested that Dr Grace did more good for his patients by dispensing common sense rather than sophisticated medicine.

In 1899, when Grace was only 51, he retired from general practice, resigning in protest at the way his practice would be affected by the proposed amalgamation of the Bristol Poor Law Unions. He then moved back to London to take the job of running the London County Cricket Club. Fourteen years later, at the start of World War I, Grace called for the immediate closure of the county cricket season and for all first-class cricketers to set an example and serve their country.

Family tragedy

W.G. Grace married Agnes Day in 1873 and they had three sons and a daughter. The family were very close and W.G. was devastated when his daughter Bessie died from typhoid at the age of 20 in 1899. He also lost his eldest son, W.G. junior, who died of appendicitis in 1905 at the age of 30. W.G. Grace died on 23 October 1915 after having a cerebral haemorrhage. His death shook the nation and *The Times* paid tribute to 'a cricket career that has not been equalled by any cricketer in the past and is not likely to be in the future'.

QUOTES FROM W.G. GRACE

'They came to see me bat, not you bowl.'
W.G. Grace putting the bails back on his stumps after being bowled first ball.

'I don't like defensive shots you can only get threes.'

'A cricketer's life is a life of splendid freedom, healthy effort, endless variety and delightful good fellowship.'

The Founder of Modern Nursing – Nurse Number 1

Ethel Manson (later Mrs Bedford Fenwick and also known as Ethel Gordon Fenwick) was Matron of Bart's from 1881 to 1887. She was a formidable Matron, who developed what was to become the world-famous Bart's training school for nurses. She is also renowned as the originator of the movement for state registered nurses.

Ethel Gordon Manson was born in Elgin, Morayshire on 26 January 1857. Her father, Dr Davidson Manson, died when Ethel was an infant, leaving her mother, Harriet, with three very young children. Late in 1859, Harriet married landed gentleman and future MP George Storer of Thornton Hall, Nottinghamshire. Ethel was educated at home and had a very happy, privileged childhood surrounded by antiques and domestic staff. She was beautiful, clever and very determined, and it may have been assumed that she was set for the social scene. Ethel, however, had other ideas and harboured secret ambitions to become a nurse and then to get married and have a family. She was not to be deterred.

In 1878, Ethel started as a paying probationer (paying £6 10 shillings a year) at the Nottinghamshire Children's Hospital. A year later she went to the Manchester Royal Infirmary to undertake her general training, after which she was appointed a ward sister at the London Hospital. In 1881, she saw an advertisement for the position of Matron at Bart's and without more ado, took her testimonials to the secretary, who was charmed by her beauty and brains and agreed to put in a good word for her. A week later, she was summoned to a Board Meeting and was informed that her application to replace Miss Machin had been successful and that her pay would be £250 p.a. The nursing care in the hospital was about to undergo a radical change.

Matron at Bart's

Ethel Manson was totally different from her predecessor. At 24, Manson was the hospital's youngest matron ever and some senior staff objected to her relative youth. She had no links with the Nightingale circle and it is thought that her appointment was a conscious decision to break with the Nightingale tradition.

NEW UNIFORMS FOR BART'S

The continuity between training and practice was shown by the introduction of new uniforms for staff nurses and probationers. The staff nurses' traditional brown dresses were gradually replaced by navy and white striped, long-sleeved dresses worn with a blue belt. Second- and third-year probationers wore the same dresses as staff nurses, but with white belts. First-year probationers wore grey dresses.

Manson's tenure at Bart's was only six years but it provided the groundwork for her future work in reorganising and raising the status of the nursing profession. Supportive of her nurses, she always demanded very high standards and visited the wards twice a day to check they were clean, tidy and efficiently run.

In 1885, Manson introduced a three-month course for special probationers, who were called 'ladies' as distinct from other candidates. This attracted women of a superior class (including the daughter of a Duke and the daughter of the Lord Mayor of London) who had sufficient funds to pay for their training and did not want the commitment of a three-year training period. By Manson's last year at Bart's she was receiving 1,500 letters of enquiry for 50 vacancies. Many of the special probationers went on to become ordinary probationers. By the end of the decade, becoming a nurse at Bart's had become socially acceptable and Bart's nurses included the daughters of architects, accountants, stock brokers, military officers and lawyers.

Structured teaching plans were implemented and in 1882 the course was extended to three years, with examinations at the end of the first and the third years. By the time Manson left Bart's she had weeded out most of the untrained sisters and only a handful remained at the hospital.

Manson became convinced of the need for her nurses to have professional independence, and felt there was a lack of protection for both the trained nurses and the public from women who called themselves nurses but had no training. She was also concerned about the exploitation of private nurses by their employers and so she set up the Trained Nurses' Institute to supply certificated Bart's nurses for private work.

Mrs Bedford Fenwick's destiny

Ethel Manson married the gynaecologist Dr Bedford Fenwick in 1887 and was obliged to leave her Matron's post. Undaunted, her ambition was coming to fruition. Her life's work was about to begin, and among her many professional achievements she became famous for campaigning tirelessly for the state registration of nurses. This was strongly opposed by Florence Nightingale and others who felt that nursing was a quasi-religious vocation for which one or two years of training were sufficient. Ethel Fenwick, supported by her husband, never gave up, and after 30 years there was a reward for this restless genius. When the register of nurses finally opened, in 1923, 'Ethel Gordon Fenwick' was listed as 'Nurse No. 1'.

TIMELINE OF ACHIEVEMENTS

1881   Bought *Nursing Record*, later renamed *British Journal of Nursing*; its Editor for 53 years

1883   Joint founder, with Isla Stewart, and first President of the International Council of Nurses

1887   Founded British Nurses' Association

1894   Joint Founder with Isla Sewart of the Matrons' Council of Great Britain and Ireland

1908   Nursing Representative, National Women's Suffrage Societies

1926   Founder and President of the British College of Nursing

1934   Inaugurated the Florence Nightingale Foundation

Final days

The Bedford Fenwicks had one son, Christian, born in 1888. During World War I, Ethel and her husband decided to give up living together, but remained on good terms until his death in 1939. She lived to a ripe old age but at 89 fractured her hip and was warded in a private room off Lawrence ward at Bart's. Back in the hospital where she had made such a difference, she 'was nursed with the greatest kindness and gentleness'. She died, aged 90, on 13 March 1947, and on 19 March a memorial service was held for her in St Bartholomew the Less.

ISLA STEWART 1855–1910

Progressive champion of the nursing profession

With Isla Stewart as Matron (1887–1910), Bart's became well known both nationally and internationally for nurse training. Stewart also played a key role in turning nursing into a profession, and founded the League of St Bartholomew's Nurses, the first organisation of its kind in the United Kingdom.

Isla Stewart was born in Scotland and lived at Slodahill, Dumfriesshire. Her father was a soldier, journalist and a Fellow of the Scottish Society of Antiquaries. He had sent his other daughters to school abroad but Isla was educated at home.

In 1879 Isla Stewart became a special probationer at the Nightingale Training School for Nurses attached to St Thomas's Hospital in London. The training was a one-year programme but after nine months Stewart was appointed Sister of a 20-bedded women's surgical ward, for which she felt ill equipped. In 1885 she became Matron of the smallpox

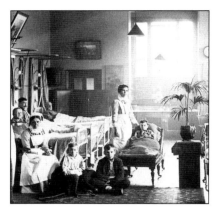

Nursing staff and patients pose for a photograph when Stewart was Matron

camp set up to cope with an epidemic at Darenth in Kent, where despite the appalling conditions and lack of trained nurses she reorganised the nursing to a high standard. She then spent a year as Matron at the Eastern Fever Hospital, Homerton.

When Stewart was 30, in 1887, the post of Matron at Bart's became vacant due to the resignation of Ethel Manson on her marriage to Dr Bedford Fenwick. Stewart wrote to her mother saying 'the biggest appointment in the nursing world is vacant, [and] I am going to try for it'. Her application was successful and she took up the position in June.

Matron of St Bartholomew's Hospital
Isla Stewart was faced by the challenge of a well organised nursing department at Bart's and a training programme already in place, and although she set

about revising and introducing new policies, she did not develop a Preliminary Training School similar to those at St Thomas's and Guy's Hospitals.

In 1894 she introduced a new training scheme where she gave classes in basic nursing to nurses during their first six months of training. These included the principles of invalid cookery, the

---

REVISED TRAINING REGULATIONS FOR NURSES AT BART'S, 1894

- Age of probationers to be 23 to 35 years
- Elementary examination to be taken as proof of general education and intelligence, including an examination in anatomy, physiology and science, before acceptance as probationers on trial
- Formal acceptance as probationers at end of trial period
- To serve the hospital for 4 years:
    - probationer for 3 years
    - certificate of competency awarded
    - staff nurse for one year
    - free to leave the hospital
- Uniform to be supplied and paid for by the hospital after trial period
- Board and lodging to be provided by the hospital
- Payments to be made quarterly (£2 per quarter in first year; £3 in second year; £5 in third year; £7 10s in fourth year)
- Failure to pass the preliminary training course examination or the first or third year examinations to lead to dismissal
- Misconduct, inefficiency, or repeated neglect of duty to lead to dismissal

basic skills of washing a patient in bed, bed making, preparation of patients for operations, and the administration of enemas. This new scheme remained in place for the next 12 years.

In 1905 the training was reviewed to take into account the developments in medicine and nursing. A six-week preliminary training course was introduced and a more detailed syllabus of lectures given throughout the nurses training, although there was no actual nursing school until 1925.

During the 23 years of Miss Stewart's matronship the working conditions of the nurses steadily improved due largely to the increase of nursing staff. Previously the day duty hours had been 7 a.m. until 9 p.m. but by the time Stewart retired she had been able to reduce the hours worked by the nurses and could have two nurses on a ward at night. Despite bringing in these improvements she did not live to see her 'wished for' nurses home.

League of St Bartholomew's Nurses

In 1899 Stewart founded, and was the first President of, the League of St Bartholomew's Nurses, open to Bart's trained nurses. Stewart's purpose was to encourage high nursing standards among its members, to help them to meet socially, and to provide support for those who had fallen on hard times. However, she had other objectives, and members were encouraged to be vocal on issues such as registration for nurses and the Suffragette Movement.

Nursing politics

When Isla Stewart was appointed Matron at Bart's she rapidly became a close friend and political ally of Ethel Bedford Fenwick. She supported Fenwick in the registration movement and Bart's gained the reputation as the most progressive of all the London hospitals for its nursing policy. The couple were joint founders of the International Council of Nurses in 1883 and the Matrons' Council of Great Britain and Ireland in 1894.

In 1901, as President of the Matrons' Council, Stewart headed a deputation to the War Office to

lobby for a new women's army nursing service. This resulted in 1902 in the formation of Queen Alexandra's Imperial Military Nursing Service (QAIMNS), established by Royal Warrant and with Queen Alexandra as its President.

Legacy

Isla Stewart was Matron of Bart's for 23 years; she was efficient, loyal, much loved and admired. Under her careful supervision, the reputation of nurse training at Bart's grew very considerably. At least as important was the contribution she made to the development of professional awareness among nurses. She remained in her post until 1910 but was already suffering ill health. Her last public appearance was at a conference on 12 February 1910 to discuss the Bill for state registration. She died shortly after, on 6 March.

A memorial service for Isla Stewart was held in the church of St Bartholomew the Great, as the hospital parish church of St Bartholomew the Less was too small to accommodate all the many people who wished to attend.

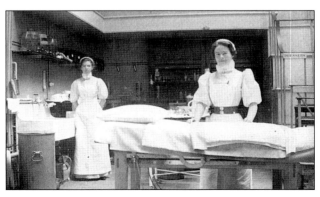

A Bart's probationer (white belt) with a staff nurse (blue belt)

BIBLIOGRAPHY

Bodington, George, *An Essay on the Treatment and Cure of Pulmonary Consumption* (Longman, Orme, Brown, Green & Longmans, London, 1840)

Cadbury, Deborah, *The Dinosaur Hunters: A True Story of Scientific Rivalry and the Discovery of the Prehistoric World* (Fourth Estate, London, 2000)

Forshaw, Alec & Bergström, Theo, *Smithfield Past & Present* (William Heinemann Ltd, London, 1980)

Forster, Margaret, *Significant Sisters: the Grassroots of Active Feminism 1839–1939* (Vintage, London, 2004)

Koven, Seth, *Slumming: Sexual Politics in Victorian London* (Princeton University Press, 2004)

Low, Robert, *W.G. Grace: An Intimate Biography* (Metro Books, London, 2004)

Main, Jenny, *The First Nurse: Ethel Bedford Fenwick* (Librario Publishing Ltd, Kinloss, 2003)

Medvei, V.C. & Thornton, J.L., eds, *The Royal Hospital of Saint Bartholomew 1123–1973* (St Bartholomew's Hospital, London, 1974)

Moore, Wendy, *The Knife Man: Blood, Body-snatching and the Birth of Modern Surgery* (Bantam Press, 2005)

Palmer, William and others, *Illustrated Life and Career of William Palmer of Rugeley* (Ward and Lock, London, 1856)

Porter, Roy, *The Greatest Benefit to Mankind: A Medical History of Humanity* (Harper Collins, London, 1997)

Sandwith, Frieda, *Surgeon Compassionate: the Story of Dr William Marsden* (Peter Davies, London, 1960)

Van der Kiste, John, *William John Wills: Pioneer of the Australian Outback* (The History Press, Stroud, Gloucestershire, 2011)

Waddington, Keir, *Medical Education at St Bartholomew's Hospital, 1123–1995* (Boydell Press, Woodbridge, Suffolk, 2003)

Yeo, Geoffrey, *Images of Bart's: Illustrated History of St Bartholomew's Hospital in the City of London* (Historical Publications Ltd, with the Archive Dept, St Bartholomew's Hospital, London, 1992)

Yeo, Geoffrey, *Nursing at Bart's: A History of Nursing Service and Nurse Education at St Bartholomew's Hospital, London* (St Bartholomew and Princess Alexandra and Newham College of Nursing and Midwifery, London, 1995; The History Press, Stroud, Gloucestershire, 1995)

ILLUSTRATION CREDITS

SCISSORS, NURSE, SCISSORS

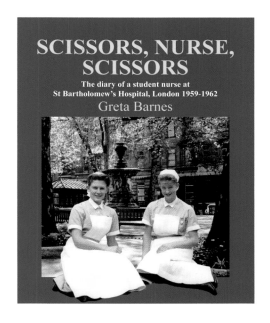

Scissors Nurse Scissors is an informative, historical and nostalgic book based on Greta Barnes' diaries from when she was a student nurse at Bart's in the 1950s and 1960s. The diaries, kept throughout her nursing training, tell a personal story with youthful freshness. They also provide a snapshot of what many of our hospitals were like at the time.

Scissors, Nurse, Scissors is illustrated with numerous photographs, many of them from the Bart's Hospital Archives.

230mm x 185mm, 96 pages, published by Obelisk Books, 2009

THE HEART OF BART'S

The Heart of Bart's is a tribute to a well loved hospital, written by people who were proud to be part of it, over a period of 50 years. Greta Barnes and her fellow contributors (mainly members of the medical and nursing professions) recollect their time at the hospital and describe their varied roles.

The Heart of Bart's was compiled to create a portrait – in words, photographs and illustrations – of a great London teaching hospital during its golden years before the turmoil of change.

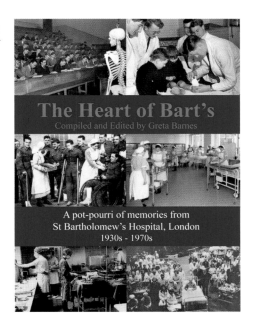

240mm x 187mm, 140 pages, published by Obelisk Books, 2011

Greta Barnes, the author of *Long Live Bart's* welcomes this opportunity to acknowledge and publicise the invaluable role of Barts Charity in helping to ensure that the Barts Health NHS Trust hospitals will continue to be at the forefront of modern medical care and research.

b+tlc BARTS CHARITY

Barts Charity can trace the very first donations made to the Hospital of St Bartholomew as far back as the 12th century.

Through St Bartholomew's Hospital and Medical School, the Charity has provided funding for some of the most significant milestones in medicine. These include the discovery of the circulatory system, the establishing of the founding principles of modern surgery, and the advancement of countless technological developments in anaesthetics, X-ray imaging and heart surgery.

Without the money raised by benefactors and donors over the past 900 years, modern medicine as we know it may have looked very different. Today, charitable funding for leading research and patient care remains as important as ever.

Barts Charity exists to support the remarkable work carried out by the doctors, nurses and staff in all of the Barts Health NHS Trust hospitals: St Bartholomew's, Royal London, London Chest, Whipps Cross, Newham and Mile End.

With the help of our donors we provide funding for a huge variety of special projects, ground-breaking research and state-of-the-art equipment that would not be funded by the NHS. The work we fund is challenging, exciting and pioneering.

If you would like to find out more about us or to support our work then please visit www.bartscharity.org.uk or call us on 0207 618 1717.